Achieving Facts Fluency

– Primary –

For use with

Math in Focus:
Singapore Math

by Marshall Cavendish

Includes:

- Basic Facts Strategies
- Basic Facts Workshop
- Basic Facts Practice Sheets

 HOUGHTON MIFFLIN HARCOURT

HOUGHTON MIFFLIN HARCOURT

Table of Contents

Level 1

Basic Facts Workshops

Level 2

Basic Facts Workshops

Level 3

Basic Facts Workshops

Achieving Facts Fluency

A Systematic Practice Plan for Basic Facts and Skills

Knowledge of basic facts and development of computational skills are essential to all areas of mathematics. Facts and skills do for math what phonics and decoding do for reading: They build fluency. *Achieving Facts Fluency* gives children opportunities throughout the school year to learn, to practice, and to master basic facts for addition, subtraction, and multiplication, as well as computational skills.

Achieving Facts Fluency is organized simply and is easy to use. Basic Facts Strategies outline each strategy for every operation for easy teacher reference. At each level, workshops with accompanying practice worksheets give children opportunities to master basic facts and skills. These are followed by Cumulative Practice pages, Answers, and Support Masters. *Achieving Facts Fluency* can be used for students who need practice with basic skills, on level skills, or advanced skills.

Instruction in Math in Focus focuses on depth of understanding and teaches both how and why operations work. Use this resource for additional practice to promote automaticity, so that in problem solving situations students are involved in higher level thinking and are not caught up with basic calculations.

Basic Facts Strategies

This section is comprised of 13 charts—4 addition, 4 subtraction, and 5 multiplication—that define and illustrate the strategies children most often use to learn basic facts. These pages familiarize teachers with the strategies that are referenced throughout the workshops. At a glance, teachers are provided with an orientation to each of the strategies and corresponding facts.

Workshops and Worksheets

Teacher-directed workshops systematically develop strategies that build understanding and facilitate recall of basic facts and development of computational skills. With the workshops, teachers can review previously taught operations. Developmentally appropriate workshops gradually foster children's self-confidence in using basic facts strategies. The two worksheets that accompany each workshop are reproducible. They provide both independent and cooperative opportunities to practice a particular skill and can be used in class or as homework.

Achieving Facts Fluency (continued)

Basic Facts Workshops

Workshops cover basic facts for addition, subtraction, and multiplication. These workshops use number patterns, visual models, and prior knowledge to introduce and to develop the strategy for learning a specific group of facts.

Children create manipulatives such as flash cards and spinners to practice basic facts independently or with a partner. Once children create and build a personal collection of flash cards for each group of facts, they can then use their own set of cards to cumulatively review and practice facts at school and at home. The Practice Minutes Records pages facilitate at-home practice of basic facts and promote family involvement in documenting student progress.

Cumulative Practice

Cumulative Practice pages can assist in basic facts practice, serve as a tool for review, or provide assessment. One way to use Cumulative Practice is to have children circle facts that belong to a specific strategy or strategies they have been studying and then have them answer only those facts. As children work toward mastery of basic facts, they can use Cumulative Practice for self-assessment. The teacher can also opt to administer the Cumulative Practice after children have demonstrated an understanding of strategies for learning basic facts.

Answers

Answers to worksheets at all levels and to the Cumulative Practice pages provide the teacher with a quick scoring reference.

Support Masters

Support Masters include workmats, spinners, templates, grids, recording sheets, certificates, and the My Math Handbook page. Easily reproducible as transparencies or for multiple copies, the Support Masters are referenced by number in the workshops under Materials.

Basic Facts Strategies

Addition

Zero in Addition

+	0	1	2	3	4	5	6	7	8	9
0	0+0	0+1	0+2	0+3	0+4	0+5	0+6	0+7	0+8	0+9
1	1+0									
2	2+0									
3	3+0									
4	4+0									
5	5+0									
6	6+0									
7	7+0									
8	8+0									
9	9+0									

When you add zero to a number, you get that number. When you add a number to zero, you get that number.

Counting on 1, 2, 3

+	0	1	2	3	4	5	6	7	8	9
0										
1		1+1	1+2	1+3	1+4	1+5	1+6	1+7	1+8	1+9
2		2+1	2+2	2+3	2+4	2+5	2+6	2+7	2+8	2+9
3		3+1	3+2	3+3	3+4	3+5	3+6	3+7	3+8	3+9
4		4+1	4+2	4+3						
5		5+1	5+2	5+3						
6		6+1	6+2	6+3						
7		7+1	7+2	7+3						
8		8+1	8+2	8+3						
9		9+1	9+2	9+3						

Put the greater number in your head– count on from there the number that the lesser number indicates. For example: 8 + 2 . . . put 8 in your head and count on . . . 9, 10.

Doubles, Near Doubles

+	0	1	2	3	4	5	6	7	8	9
0										
1										
2										
3										
4					4 + 4	4 + 5	4 + 6			
5					5 + 4	5 + 5	5 + 6	5 + 7		
6					6 + 4	6 + 5	6 + 6	6 + 7	6 + 8	
7						7 + 5	7 + 6	7 + 7	7 + 8	7 + 9
8							8 + 6	8 + 7	8 + 8	8 + 9
9								9 + 7	9 + 8	9 + 9

Memorize doubles, then use them to figure out the near doubles. For example: "I know that 6 + 6 = 12, so 6 + 5 must be one less, or 11, and 6 + 7 must be one more, or 13."

Making a Ten

+	0	1	2	3	4	5	6	7	8	9
0										
1										
2										
3										
4								4 + 7	4 + 8	4 + 9
5									5 + 8	5 + 9
6										6 + 9
7					7 + 4					
8					8 + 4	8 + 5				
9					9 + 4	9 + 5	9 + 6			

9 + 5
One more makes ten
and 4 more makes 14. ➡

Basic Facts Strategies

Subtraction

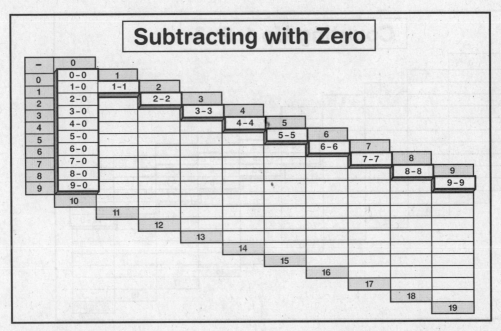

Subtracting with Zero

When you subtract zero from any number, you get the same number. When you subtract any number from itself you get zero.

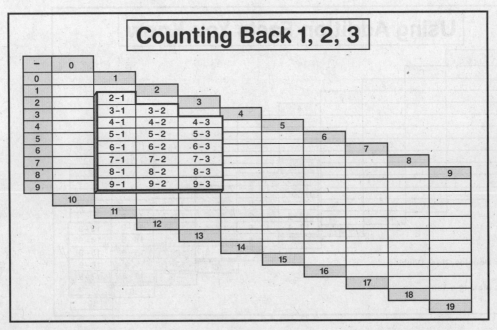

Counting Back 1, 2, 3

Put the greater number in your head. Count back the number of places indicated by the lesser number. For example: 6 − 2 . . . put 6 in your head and count back . . . 5, 4.

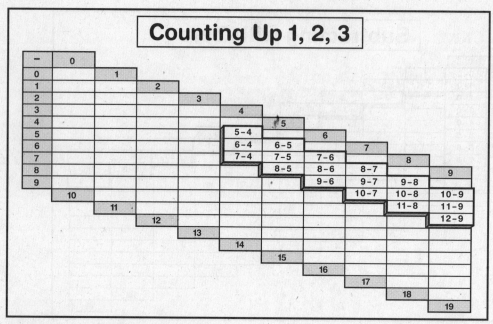

Counting Up 1, 2, 3

For example: 7 – 5. Start with the lesser number and keep track of how many numbers you count to get the greater number. Put 5 in you head, count . . . 6, 7– it took two numbers to get from 5 to 7 so the answer is 2.

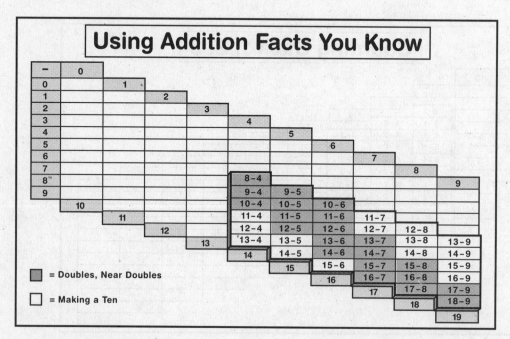

Using Addition Facts You Know

■ = Doubles, Near Doubles

□ = Making a Ten

Use Doubles, Near Doubles and Making a Ten addition strategies to find these facts.

Basic Facts Strategies
Multiplication

Properties (0's, 1's)

x	0	1	2	3	4	5	6	7	8	9
0	0x0	0x1	0x2	0x3	0x4	0x5	0x6	0x7	0x8	0x9
1	1x0	1x1	1x2	1x3	1x4	1x5	1x6	1x7	1x8	1x9
2	2x0	2x1								
3	3x0	3x1								
4	4x0	4x1								
5	5x0	5x1								
6	6x0	6x1								
7	7x0	7x1								
8	8x0	8x1								
9	9x0	9x1								

Any fact in which zero is a factor results in a product of zero. The product of one times any factor is that factor.

Skip Counting (3's, 5's)

x	0	1	2	3	4	5	6	7	8	9
0										
1										
2						2x5				
3				3x3	3x4	3x5	3x6	3x7	3x8	3x9
4				4x3		4x5				
5			5x2	5x3	5x4	5x5	5x6	5x7	5x8	5x9
6				6x3		6x5				
7				7x3		7x5				
8				8x3		8x5				
9				9x3		9x5				

Skip-count by 3's and by 5's to find these facts.

Doubles (2's, 4's)

x	0	1	2	3	4	5	6	7	8	9
0										
1										
2			2x2	2x3	2x4		2x6	2x7	2x8	2x9
3			3x2							
4			4x2		4x4		4x6	4x7	4x8	4x9
5										
6			6x2		6x4					
7			7x2		7x4					
8			8x2		8x4					
9			9x2		9x4					

In this strategy, relate learning the 2's to learning the 4's. For example, since $2 \times 3 = 6$, then 4×3 is double 6, or 12.

Using Tens (9's)

x	0	1	2	3	4	5	6	7	8	9
0										
1										
2										2x9
3										3x9
4										4x9
5										5x9
6										6x9
7										7x9
8										8x9
9			9x2	9x3	9x4	9x5	9x6	9x7	9x8	9x9

Use multiplying by 10 to multiply by 9. For example, to find 7×9 think $7 \times 10 = 70$. Subtract the 7, the factor that is not a multiple of 10, from the product ($70 - 7 = 63$).

Achieving Facts Fluency **Basic Facts Strategies**

Use What You Know (6's, 7's, 8's)

x	0	1	2	3	4	5	6	7	8	9
0										
1										
2										
3										
4										
5										
6							6x6	6x7	6x8	6x9
7							7x6	7x7	7x8	7x9
8							8x6	8x7	8x8	8x9
9							9x6	9x7	9x8	9x9

Previous strategies have introduced facts for 6, 7, and 8 multiplied by 1, 2, 3, 4, 5, and 9. The remaining facts to be learned are 6×6, 6×7, 6×8, 7×7, 7×8, and 8×8. Use patterns from other facts.

Basic Facts Strategies
Division

Students can master most division facts from previously–learned multiplication facts. There are two uses of 1 in division.

Dividing by 1
Any number divided by 1 is that number.
Example: $7 \div 1 = 7$

Dividing by All
Any number divided by itself is 1.
Example: $7 \div 7 = 1$

Math in Focus Correlation

Level 1

Basic Facts Workshops pp. 12-35

Basic Facts Practice Worksheets pp. 36-59

Level 2

Basic Facts Workshops pp. 60-83

Basic Facts Practice Worksheets pp. 84-107

Level 3

Basic Facts Workshops pp. 108-119

1. Addition and Subtraction Facts . . . . Grade 1, Chapters 3 & 4
2. Doubles, Near Doubles Addition and Subtract Facts . . . . Grade 1, Chapter 8
3. Using Ten to Add and Subtract . . . . Grade 1, Chapter 8
4. Naming and Using Arrays in Multiplication . . . . Grade 2, Chapters 5 & 6
5. Multiplying by 1 and 2 . . . . Grade 2, Chapter 6
6. Multiplying by 4 . . . . Grade 2, Chapter 15
7. Multiplying by 3 . . . . Grade 2, Chapter 15
8. Multiplying by 6 . . . . Grade 2, Chapter 15; Grade 3, Chapter 6
9. Multiplying by 5 . . . . Grade 2, Chapter 6
10. Multiplying by 9 . . . . Grade 2, Chapter 6; Grade 3, Chapter 6
11. Multiplying by 7 . . . . Grade 3, Chapter 6
12. Multiplying by 8 . . . . Grade 3, Chapter 6

Basic Facts Practice Worksheets pp. 120-143

1A-1B. Addition and Subtraction Facts . . . . Grade 1, Chapters 3 & 4
2A-2B. Doubles, Near Doubles Addition and Subtraction Facts . . . . Grade 1, Chapter 8
3A-3B. Using Ten to Add and Subtract . . . . Grade 1, Chapter 8
4A-4B. Naming and Using Arrays in Multiplication . . . . Grade 1, Chapters 5 & 6
5A-5B. Multiplying by 1 and 2 . . . . Grade 1, Chapter 6
6A-6B. Multiplying by 4 . . . . Grade 2, Chapter 15
7A-7B. Multiplying by 3 . . . . Grade 2, Chapter 15
8A-8B. Multiplying by 6 . . . . Grade 2, Chapter 15; Grade 3, Chapter 6
9A-9B. Multiplying by 5 . . . . Grade 2, Chapter 6
10A-10B. Multiplying by 9 . . . . Grade 2, Chapter 6; Grade 3, Chapter 6
11A-11B. Multiplying by 7 . . . . Grade 3, Chapter 6
12A-12B. Multiplying by 8 . . . . Grade 3, Chapter 6

Basic Facts Workshop 1

Readiness: Counting

Introduce It!

20 minutes

Counting Names

Management whole class
Materials name card per child, one set of number cards 1–10

- Hold up each child's name card individually and have the child read it. Ask the class to count the number of letters in the name. Then have the child retrieve the name card.

- When all cards have been distributed, hold up a number card. Ask all of the children with that many letters in their name to stand up. Then have them sit down. Have classmates help one another to decide

when to stand. Repeat with other numbers until every child has had a turn to get up.

- Ask, Which number of letters in a name is the largest group in our class? Which number of letters is the smallest group in our class? How can we be sure? **Count the members of each group.**

Tips

You may want to count children as they stand and record the number of children in each group.

Develop It!

25 minutes

Putting Names Together

Management whole class
Materials name card per child

- Ask a pair of children to stand up with their name cards. Have classmates count how many letters are in both names together. Repeat several times with different pairs of children.

- Have children form two lines so each child has a partner. Have each pair, in turn, hold up their name cards and tell how many letters are in their two names together.

- After each pair reports their combined name count, ask the front child in one line to go to the back of that line. Have everyone else in that line step forward to find a new partner.

- New partners may find the total number of letters in their combined names and report to the class. Continue the activity by asking the front child in the same line to step to the back of that line.

Tips

If children know how many letters are in their names, they may count on their partner's letters for a total.

Name Chart

🕐 **15 minutes**

Management individuals

Materials chart paper, adding machine tape or grid strips, construction paper

- Cut and distribute lengths of adding machine tape (which has been pre-divided into squares) or grid strips to each child. Ask them how many squares they need to write the letters of their first name.

- Have children print their first names on the strips, glue the strips to construction paper, and write the number of letters.

- The children place their names on the chart according to the number of letters in them. They can paste their names in place on the chart for a class record.

Tips

Remind children to write each letter of their name in a separate square on the strip.

Basic Facts Workshop 2

Readiness: The Ten-Frame Model

 Introduce It!

⏱ **15 minutes**

Organizing Numbers

Management whole class
Materials overhead projector, transparency of ten frame, counters

- Place ten counters randomly on the overhead projector. Quickly turn the projector on and off. Ask children how many counters they saw.

- Turn the projector back on and count the number of counters together, touching a counter as each number is said.

- Explain that it would be easier to tell how many there are if the counters were organized. Show the ten-frame transparency on the overhead.

- Why do you think this is called a ten frame? **There are ten boxes.** If I put one counter in each box, how many counters will I use? **10** Place counters in the top row of the ten frame from left to right, then in the bottom row as children count with you.

- Ask volunteers to show other numbers on the ten frame. Have the class identify how many counters are shown, and tell how many more are needed to make a ten.

 Develop It!

⏱ **15 minutes**

Count, Write, and Switch

Management pairs
Materials overhead projector, transparency of ten frame, counters

- Have children work with a partner.

- Using the overhead projector, put counters on the ten frame to show a number from 1 to 10.

- One child writes the numeral that tells how many counters they see. The partner checks for accuracy. Children then switch roles.

- Repeat the activity several times so each partner will have an opportunity to write most numerals from 1–10.

Tips

This is another opportunity to check on the progress of children's numeral-writing skills.

Ten-Frame Practice

20 minutes

Management pairs
Materials 12 index cards, counters, ten frames

- Distribute 12 index cards to pairs of children. Have them write the numerals 1-12, one on each card.

- Distribute a ten frame and 12 counters to each pair.

- Ask pairs to mix their number cards and place them face-down. As one child turns over a card, the partner shows that number with counters on the ten frame. Children can check their results, then switch roles.

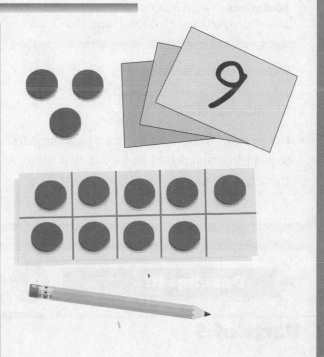

Tips

Have children retain their ten frames for future use.

Basic Facts Workshop 3
Readiness: Part-Part-Whole Model

 Introduce It!

15 minutes

Introducing Parts and Whole

Management whole class
Materials overhead projector, teacher-made transparency of part-part-whole mat (Achieving Facts Fluency Support Master 2), 6 counters

- Show six counters on the projector. Place them at the top of the part-part-whole transparency. Ask children how many they see. **6**

- Pick up the six counters and drop them on the projector so they fall on both sides of the line. Ask, How many counters are on this side? That's one part of six. How many are on the other side? That's the other part of six.

- Remind children that this shows two parts (e.g. two and four) that make up the whole, six. We can show other parts that make up the whole, six.

- Repeat several times by shaking and dropping the counters to show a variety of part-part-whole relationships for six.

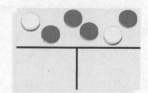 

 Tips

Have children state each relationship.

 Develop It!

15 minutes

Parts of 5

Management individuals
Materials chart paper, 5 counters per child

- Have each child take five counters and shake them in both hands. Then tell children to open their hands with some counters in each.

- Ask children to describe how the counters in their hands show five. For example, three counters and two counters make five counters in all. Draw two hands on chart paper or on the chalkboard, and write the numeral 5 above them. Below the hands, record each combination of five as children report it. (3 and 2, 1 and 4, 0 and 5, etc.)

- Have children shake their counters again, and then open their hands and describe the new configuration. Repeat several times and continue recording.

  Tips

Have children describe all the possible ways to show five.

Make It!

15 minutes

Hands Mat

Management pairs

Materials file folders, construction paper, scissors, glue, 6 two-sided counters per child

- Have each child make a hands mat. Children should work in pairs to trace each other's hands on construction paper.

- Children can glue cut-out hands to construction paper or file folders, which can be used later for storing children's work.

- Distribute six counters to each child. The child shakes the counters in both hands, drops them and puts all of one color on one construction paper hand, the rest on the other one. Then the child reports, "I have three red and three white, I have six in all," for example.

- This activity may be used repeatedly over time to give children experience with the part-part-whole model. Use different numbers of counters each time, and show children how to record as they become ready.

- Collect and save hands mats to use in future workshops.

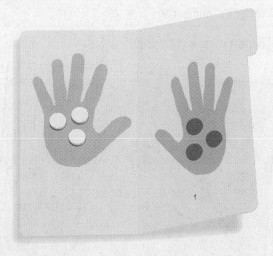

Tips

Show children who are ready, how to print numerals to record the whole and the two parts on paper. Save hands mats for future workshops.

Basic Facts Workshop 4

Readiness: Part-Part-Whole Model

Introduce It!

20 minutes

Parts of 10

Management whole class
Materials overhead projector, teacher-made transparency of part-part-whole mat (Achieving Facts Fluency Support Master 2), 10 overhead pennies

- Place ten pennies on the "whole" section of the part-part-whole transparency. Ask children how many they see. **ten** Remove the pennies and write the number 10.

- Place six pennies on one part of the mat. Ask, How many pennies do you see? **six** If there are ten pennies in all and one part is six, how many are in the other part? **four**

- Place four pennies in the other part. Move both parts into the whole section and count to verify a total of ten. Remove the pennies. Record the parts on the transparency as you say, 6 and 4 make 10. Ask a volunteer to record the matching number sentence.

  6 + 4 = 10

- Repeat with other names for ten.

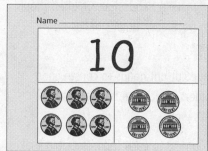

Develop It!

15 minutes

Heads and Tails

Management pairs
Materials hands mats (from Workshop 3: two hands traced on paper), 10 pennies per pair

- Provide each pair of children with ten pennies and a hands mat. Children take turns shaking ten pennies and placing them on the mat, separating the coins into heads and tails.

- Ask children to "read" their mats, naming the two parts and the whole (e.g., I have 3 heads and 7 tails. That's 10 in all.) Record responses on the chalkboard under the number 10.

- Repeat using nine coins, having children "read" their mats, and recording combinations on the chalkboard under the number 9.

- Repeat using eight coins.

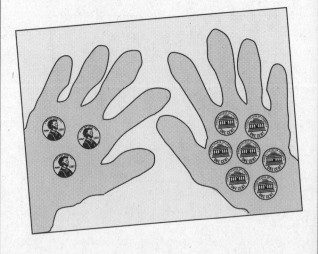

Make It!

20 minutes

Heads and Tails Charts

Management small groups
Materials 10 pennies and one hands mat per group, 6 sheets of chart paper with headings

- Divide the class into six groups. Each group will be responsible for making a chart for a different number from five to ten.

- Distribute one chart to each group. Pre-record headings on charts with one of the numbers 5, 6, 7, 8, 9, or 10 at the top. Under the number, write the headings *Heads* and *Tails*.

- Each group uses the number of pennies shown at the top of their chart. They take turns shaking and separating heads and tails, and recording all of the different combinations.

- When finished, groups may report combinations they found to the class.

	8
Heads	Tails
8	0
5	3
4	4
2	6
7	1
3	5
6	2

Tips

For further practice, have each group repeat the activity with a different number, then compare their chart with the previously made chart for that number. Did they find any new combinations?

Basic Facts Workshop 5

Readiness: Exploring Zero

 Introduce It!

15 minutes

Zeros in Addition

Management whole class
Materials overhead projector and marker, blank transparency, ten counters

- Show four counters on a blank transparency on the projector. Ask children how many they see. **four** Tell children you're going to add counters while they close their eyes. Do not add any counters. Ask children to open their eyes and identify how many counters you added. **none** What number tells how many I added? **zero** Write $4 + 0 = 4$.

- Next show five counters on the transparency. Follow the same procedure as above but when children close their eyes, move the five counters around into a new configuration. Ask, How many are there in all? **five** What number tells how many I added? **zero** Write $5 + 0 = 5$.

- Repeat with children taking turns showing from 1–9 counters and adding zero. Record the appropriate number sentence each time.

$5 + 0 = 5$

 Tips

If children seem ready, ask them to write the number sentences.

 Develop It!

15 minutes

Zeros in Subtraction

Management whole class
Materials overhead projector and marker, blank transparency, ten counters

- Show five counters on a blank transparency on the projector. Ask children how many they see. **five** Remove all five counters. Ask children how many you took away. **five** Ask children what number tells how many counters are left. **zero** Write $5 - 5 = 0$.

- Repeat with a few numbers 1–9, removing all counters each time and recording the number sentences.

- Show three counters. Ask how many children see. **three** Tell children you are going to take some away while they close their eyes. Do not remove any counters. Ask children how many counters are left and what number tells how many you took away. **three, zero** Write $3 - 0 = 3$. Repeat with other numbers.

 Tips

Ask a volunteer to come up and "take away" zero from a number of counters.

Make It!

Make a Zero Spinner

Management pairs

Materials 3-part spinner (Achieving Facts Fluency Support
Master 5, paper clip, and ten counters per pair

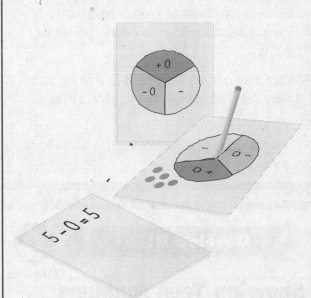

- Distribute a 3-part spinner, a paper clip, and 10 counters to each pair of children. Have them write +0, −0, and − in the three spinner sections.

- Show children how to use a paper clip and a pencil to create a spinner.

- One partner selects any number of counters and places them on the table. The other partner spins the spinner to determine and carry out an action (add 0, subtract 0, or subtract all counters.)

- The first partner records the number sentence.

- Repeat, with partners taking turns.

Tips

Initially, monitor groups to make sure they are carrying out the appropriate action and recording the number sentences.

Basic Facts Workshop 6

Readiness: Double Ten-Frames

Introduce It!

15 minutes

Ten and More

Management whole class

Materials overhead projector, teacher-made double ten-frame transparency (Achieving Facts Fluency Support Master 3), 20 overhead counters in 2 colors (10 each)

- Fill the top ten frame on a double ten-frame transparency. Ask children how many counters they see. **10**

- Place three counters of a second color on the bottom frame. Ask children how many they see. **3** Write 10 + 3.

- How many counters are there in all? Write the sum. **13**

- Clear all counters from the ten frames.

- Write 15. Ask the class how to show that number on the ten frames. **10 on the top, 5 on the bottom** Write 10 + 5 = 15

- Repeat with 14, 16, and 17.

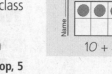

10 + 3 = 13

Tips

This is a good opportunity to ask children whether they notice a pattern in the number sentences. Encourage them to describe patterns.

Develop It!

15 minutes

Showing Teen Numbers

Management pairs

Materials each pair needs: double ten-frame workmat (Achieving Facts Fluency Support Master 3), 19 counters

- Distribute a double ten-frame workmat and 19 counters to each pair.

- Write 14. Ask pairs to show 14 on their workmats. **10 on the top frame, 4 on the bottom**

- Write 17 and say, Now show me 17.

- Repeat, having pairs show 18, 15, 13, 12, and 16.

- Watch for pairs who remove or add counters without

clearing the mats and starting over. Ask these pairs to share their strategy. **All of the teen numbers have 10 and some more, so it saves time to leave the top frame filled.**

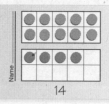

14

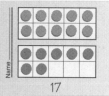

17

Tips

Suggest that as children work in pairs, they take turns showing answers so that both children have an opportunity to participate.

Make It!

20 minutes

Spin and Show

Management pairs

Materials each pair needs: 20 counters, paper clip, pencil, double ten-frame workmat and 6-section spinner (Achieving Facts Fluency Support Masters 3 and 6)

- Distribute spinners and have children label the sections 12, 13, 14, 16, 17, and 18.

- Remind children how to use a pencil and paper clip to create an arrow that attaches to the spinner.

- Distribute a double ten-frame workmat and counters to each pair.

- One partner spins to select a teen number, and the other partner models the number on the double ten-frame workmat and records (for example, 10 + 2 = 12).

- Partners switch roles. Each partner should have at least ten turns.

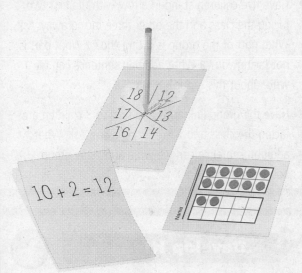

Tips

Note which pairs continue to use the strategy of leaving ten counters on the top frame and adding to the bottom frame only.

Basic Facts Workshop 7

Readiness: Order Property

Introduce It!

15 minutes

Front and Back

Management whole class
Materials none

- Have five children stand in a row with the first two facing the class and the other three facing away. Ask, What part of the group is facing you? **2** What part is not facing you? **3** What addition sentence can we write about this group? **2 + 3 = 5**

- Have the group link arms and turn so 3 children are facing the class and 2 are facing away. Ask, What addition sentence can we write about the group now? **3 + 2 = 5**

- Ask children what they notice about these addition sentences. **The numbers are in different order, but there are still five in all.**

- Repeat the activity with other groups of children to model 4 + 3 = 7 and 3 + 4 = 7; 1 + 2 = 3 and 2 + 1 = 3; and 5 + 3 = 8 and 3 + 5 = 8.

Tips

If some children have difficulty understanding the order property, review the concept of joining sets.

Develop It!

15 minutes

Flip and Record

Management whole class
Materials connecting cubes in two colors

- Show the class a cube train with two cubes of one color and four cubes of another color.

- Ask a volunteer to write a number sentence on the chalkboard to name the train. **2 + 4 = 6**

- Flip the cube train over and ask the volunteer to write the new number sentence. **4 + 2 = 6**

- Repeat the activity with cube trains for 8 + 2 and 2 + 8; 3 + 4 and 4 + 3; 5 + 1 and 1 + 5; and 4 + 5 and 5 + 4.

2+4=6   4+2=6

Tips

Children may benefit from additional practice by working with a partner to make their own cube trains and writing the corresponding number sentences.

Make It!

Practice Recording Order

20 minutes

Management whole class
Materials index cards, large paper clips

- Distribute one index card and some paper clips to each child.

- Each child should model one addition sentence by attaching paper clips to opposite edges of the card.

- Have one child show a card to the class. Each child writes the appropriate number sentence. Then, the child flips the card over and the class writes a second number sentence.

- Each child shares his or her card, then flips it, and the class writes both number sentences.

$$4+6=10$$
$$6+4=10$$

Tips

Extend practicing the order property with classroom objects.

Basic Facts Workshop 8

Strategy: Counting On to Add

Introduce It!

15 minutes

Counting on 1, 2, 3

Management whole class
Materials 10 counters, paper bag

- Hold up a set of five counters. Ask the class how many they see. Write 5 on the chalkboard. Put the counters in a paper bag one at a time as you count up to five.

- Hold up two more counters. Ask children how they can count on to find how many counters there are in all. Say, Put the five in your head, count on. . .five, six, seven. Put the last two counters in the bag as you count on. Write 5 + 2 = 7.

- Repeat the activity, having children count on to find 6 + 3, 4 + 1, 7 + 3, 5 + 2, and 8 + 1.

Tips

Help make connections to children's own lives by asking them to name situations when they might count on to add.

Develop It!

25 minutes

Spin and Count On

Management pairs
Materials each pair needs: 3-section spinner and 6-section spinner (Achieving Facts Fluency Support Masters 5 and 6), 2 paper clips, and 2 pencils

- Distribute the 3-section and 6-section spinners to each pair.

- Have them write 4, 5, 6, 7, 8, 9 on the 6-section spinner and +1, +2, +3 on the 3-section spinner.

- Distribute paper clips and pencils for children to make a pointer-arrow for each of the two spinners.

- One partner spins both spinners. The other partner records an addition sentence. (Example: 6 + 3 = 9)

- Partners switch roles. Repeat until each partner has had at least ten turns.

Tips

A common error children make is not beginning with the greater addend. Help them to see that it is easier to count on from the greater addend.

Make It!

30 minutes

Make Counting On Flash Cards

> **Management** individuals
>
> **Materials** for each child: 45 white index cards, envelope or plastic bag, practice minutes record and certificate (Achieving Facts Fluency Support Masters 9 and 13)

- Have children make flash cards as shown.

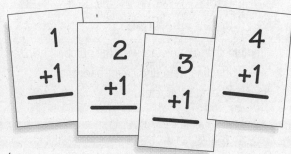

$$
\begin{array}{cccccccccc}
5 & 6 & 7 & 8 & 9 & 1 & 1 & 1 & 1 \\
+1 & +1 & +1 & +1 & +1 & +2 & +3 & +4 & +5
\end{array}
$$

$$
\begin{array}{ccccccccc}
1 & 1 & 1 & 1 & 2 & 3 & 4 & 5 & 6 \\
+6 & +7 & +8 & +9 & +2 & +2 & +2 & +2 & +2
\end{array}
$$

$$
\begin{array}{ccccccccc}
7 & 8 & 9 & 2 & 2 & 2 & 2 & 2 & 2 \\
+2 & +2 & +2 & +3 & +4 & +5 & +6 & +7 & +8
\end{array}
$$

$$
\begin{array}{ccccccccc}
2 & 3 & 3 & 3 & 3 & 3 & 3 & 3 & 4 \\
+9 & +3 & +4 & +5 & +6 & +7 & +8 & +9 & +3
\end{array}
$$

$$
\begin{array}{ccccc}
5 & 6 & 7 & 8 & 9 \\
+3 & +3 & +3 & +3 & +3
\end{array}
$$

- When finished, children can work with a partner to use their flash cards to practice counting on to add.

- Children may continue to practice at home, recording practice minutes.

- The completed practice minutes record may be exchanged for a certificate.

Tips

Remind children to initial their flash cards so they do not become mixed up with classmates' cards.

Basic Facts Workshop 9
Strategy: Counting Back to Subtract

Introduce It!

20 minutes

Counting Back 1, 2, 3

Management whole class
Materials overhead projector, 10 counters, large index card

- Place seven counters on the projector and cover them with a card. Tell the class you have covered seven counters.

- Move two counters into view.

- Ask, How many counters did I cover? **7** How many counters did I show? **2** To find how many are still covered, start at 7 and count back 2. Think 7... count 6, 5.

- Remove the card to show the answer. Write 7 − 2 = 5.

- Repeat the activity to model 5 − 1, 8 − 2, 7 − 3, 9 − 2, 6 − 1, and 9 − 3.

Tips

Remind children to start with the number they are subtracting from and count back the number being subtracted.

Develop It!

20 minutes

Spin and Count Back

Management pairs
Materials each pair needs: 2 paper clips and two pencils, 3-section spinner and 6-section spinner (Achieving Facts Fluency Support Masters 5 and 6)

- Distribute a 3-section and a 6-section spinner to each pair.

- Have children write −1, −2, −3 on the 3-section spinner, and 12, 11, 10, 9, 8, 7 on the 6-section spinner.

- Distribute paper clips and pencils for children to make a pointer for each of the spinners.

- One partner spins each spinner. The other partner records a number sentence using the two numbers.

- Partners switch roles. Each partner should have at least ten turns.

Tips

Children who need additional support may want to use counters to act out the number sentences.

Make It!

20 minutes

Make Counting Back Flash Cards

Management individuals or pairs

Materials 21 white index cards for each child, practice minutes record and certificate (Achieving Facts Fluency Support Masters 10 and 14)

- Have children make flash cards as shown below.

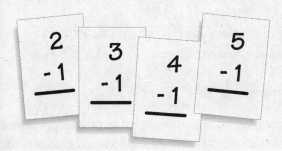

$$\begin{array}{cccccccc} 2 & 3 & 4 & 5 & 6 & 7 & 8 & 9 \\ -1 & -1 & -1 & -1 & -1 & -1 & -1 & -1 \\ \hline \end{array}$$

$$\begin{array}{ccccccc} 3 & 4 & 5 & 6 & 7 & 8 & 9 \\ -2 & -2 & -2 & -2 & -2 & -2 & -2 \\ \hline \end{array}$$

$$\begin{array}{cccccc} 4 & 5 & 6 & 7 & 8 & 9 \\ -3 & -3 & -3 & -3 & -3 & -3 \\ \hline \end{array}$$

- When finished, children should find a partner and use their flash cards to practice subtracting by counting back.

- Children may combine these flash cards with the previously made flash cards and continue practice at home, recording practice minutes.

- Completed practice records may be returned to school to be exchanged for a certificate.

Tips

Remind children to write their initials or names on the back of each card.

29

Basic Facts Workshop 10

Strategy: Counting Up to Subtract

 Introduce It!

15 minutes

Count Up If It's Close

Management whole class
Materials overhead projector, teacher-made part-part-whole transparency (Achieving Facts Fluency Support Master 2), 12 counters

- Show nine counters on the whole section of the transparency. Ask children how many they see. Write 9.

- Cover the transparency with a sheet of paper. Slide seven counters to one part of the mat and two counters to the other part.

- Reveal the seven counters and have children count them. Remind them you started with 9 and they know one part is 7.

- Ask, How many counters are in the other part? One way to find out is to count up. Start with 7, think 8, 9. How many did you count up? **2** Reveal the two counters and then write $9-7=2$.

- Repeat the activity for $7-4$, $8-6$, $6-5$, and $7-5$.

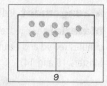
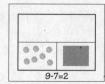

Tips

To check whether children understand the part-part-whole concept, ask volunteers to name and discuss the parts and the whole of each number sentence.

 Develop It!

20 minutes

Count Up Trains

Management whole class
Materials 12 connecting cubes

- Show the class a train of nine cubes, then put it behind your back.

- Keep three cubes behind your back and show children the train of six cubes. Remind children you started with nine and broke off six.

- Ask, How many are hiding behind my back? **3** Have children explain how they knew the answer. **Possible answer: I started with 6, then counted 7, 8, 9. That is 3 more.**

- Ask a volunteer to write a number sentence showing the whole, the part he or she knew, and the part that was determined. $9 - 6 = 3$.

- Repeat the activity for $12-9$, $8-6$, $11-9$, $7-4$, and $8-7$.

Tips

By asking children to explain the strategy they used, you can assess how well children use the counting up strategy as well as other strategies.

Make It!

Make Count Up
Flash Cards

30 minutes

Management individuals

Materials for each child: 18 orange index cards, practice minutes record, certificate (Achieving Facts Fluency Support Masters 9 and 13)

- Distribute index cards. Have children make flash cards for the facts shown here.

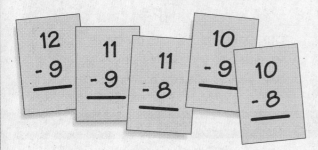

$$
\begin{array}{ccccccc}
10 & 9 & 9 & 9 & 8 & 8 & 8 \\
-7 & -8 & -7 & -6 & -7 & -6 & -5 \\
\hline
\end{array}
$$

$$
\begin{array}{cccccc}
7 & 7 & 7 & 6 & 6 & 5 \\
-6 & -5 & -4 & -5 & -4 & -4 \\
\hline
\end{array}
$$

- When finished, children should find a partner and use their flash cards to practice subtraction by counting up.

- After practicing at school, children may continue practicing at home, recording practice minutes and returning the record to school to be exchanged for a certificate.

Tips

Store flash cards in numbered plastic bags. If children are assigned one number for the year, they can quickly retrieve their numbered bag. Use for other manipulatives as well.

Basic Facts Workshop 11
Strategy: Using Doubles to Add

Introduce It!
15 minutes

Unfolding Doubles

Management whole class
Materials construction paper, hole puncher

- Fold a piece of construction paper in half and punch six holes. Ask children to count the number of holes in the paper.

- Ask the class how many holes the paper will have when it is opened. **12**

- Have children identify the number sentence shown by the unfolded paper. Write 6+6=12 on the chalkboard.

- Repeat the activity with the doubles for 5, 7, 4, 9 and 8.

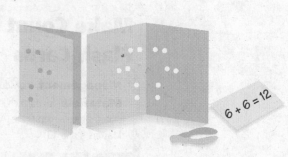

6 + 6 = 12

Tips
It may take several rounds of practice before some children understand that the number of holes doubles when the paper is opened.

Develop It!
20 minutes

Doubles and One More

Management whole class
Materials construction paper with holes from Part 1, hole puncher

- Hold up the paper from the first activity that shows double sevens. Ask the class to name the doubles fact shown, then write 7+7=14 on the chalkboard.

- Punch another hole in one side of the paper. Ask children what fact is shown now. Write 7+8=15.

- Ask children how knowing the double can help you find the double plus-1 fact. **7 + 7 = 14, so 7 + 8 is one more, or 15.**

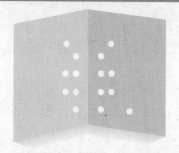

7 + 8 = 15

- Write 7+6 on the chalkboard. Ask children what double can help to find this fact. **6 + 6 and one more; 7 + 7 and one less is also acceptable**

- Write the following facts on the chalkboard: 4+5, 5+6, 8+7, 6+7, 9+8

- Ask children to identify doubles that can help them give the answers to the number expressions. Then ask, Can you think of a double that will help you find the answer to two of these number expressions at once?

30 minutes

Make Doubles Flash Cards

Management .individuals

Materials for each child: 16 blue index cards, practice minutes record and certificate (Achieving Facts Fluency Support Masters 9 and 13)

- Distribute index cards and have children make a flash card for each of the facts shown here.

$$\begin{array}{cc} 4 \\ +4 \end{array} \quad \begin{array}{cc} 4 \\ +5 \end{array} \quad \begin{array}{cc} 5 \\ +4 \end{array} \quad \begin{array}{cc} 5 \\ +5 \end{array} \quad \begin{array}{cc} 5 \\ +6 \end{array}$$

$$\begin{array}{cccccc} 6 & 6 & 6 & 7 & 7 & 7 \\ +5 & +6 & +7 & +6 & +7 & +8 \end{array}$$

$$\begin{array}{ccccc} 8 & 8 & 8 & 9 & 9 \\ +7 & +8 & +9 & +8 & +9 \end{array}$$

- Working with a partner, children should use their flash cards to practice adding with doubles.

- Children may continue at home, recording practice minutes and returning the completed record to school to be exchanged for a certificate.

Tips

Create a special time for review. Take 10 minutes and have children review facts using different sets of flash cards.

Basic Facts Workshop 12

Strategy: Using Doubles to Subtract

Introduce It!

15 minutes

Doubles Are No Trouble

Management whole class
Materials overhead projector, several teacher-made part-part-whole transparencies (Achieving Facts Fluency Support Master 2), 20 counters

- Show eight counters on the whole section of a part-part-whole transparency. Ask children how many they see.

- Ask children how many of the eight counters should go on each part if we want to have equal parts. **4** Slide the counters down.

- Cover one part with paper. Then ask children, If the whole is 8 and we know one part is 4, what is the other part? **4** Write $8-4=4$.

- Repeat, using 10, 12, 6, 14, 18, and 16 counters to identify wholes and parts, and write subtraction sentences.

Tips

Help children to first notice and then describe any patterns they see when doubling numbers.

Develop It!

15 minutes

Near Doubles and the Missing Part

Management whole class
Materials overhead projector, several teacher-made part-part-whole transparencies (Achieving Facts Fluency Support Master 2), 20 counters

- Show nine counters on the whole section of a part-part-whole transparency. Ask children how many they see.

- Cover the transparency with paper and slide the counters down, putting four on one part and five on the other part. Uncover the transparency to show four counters on one part.

- Write $9 - 4 =$. Remind children you started with 9 and they know one part is 4.

- Ask children to determine the other part. Emphasize they should think about doubles to find the missing part. Then ask, Could it be 4? **No** Why? **4 and 4 is only 8. We need one more, or 5, to make 9.**

- Complete the number sentence $9-4=5$.

- Then, write $9 - 5 =$ ___. Ask, How could you find the missing part using doubles? **5 and 5 is 10 and 1 less is 4.**

- Repeat using other examples.

Make It!

30 minutes

Make Doubles Subtraction Flash Cards

Management individuals or pairs

Materials Each child needs: 16 blue index cards, previously made set of flash cards, practice minutes record and certificate (Achieving Facts Fluency Support Masters 10 and 14)

- Distribute index cards and have children make flash cards for the doubles and near-doubles facts shown.

$$\begin{array}{c} 8 \\ -4 \\ \hline \end{array} \quad \begin{array}{c} 9 \\ -4 \\ \hline \end{array} \quad \begin{array}{c} 9 \\ -5 \\ \hline \end{array} \quad \begin{array}{c} 10 \\ -5 \\ \hline \end{array} \quad \begin{array}{c} 11 \\ -6 \\ \hline \end{array}$$

$$\begin{array}{c} 11 \\ -5 \\ \hline \end{array} \quad \begin{array}{c} 12 \\ -6 \\ \hline \end{array} \quad \begin{array}{c} 13 \\ -6 \\ \hline \end{array} \quad \begin{array}{c} 13 \\ -7 \\ \hline \end{array} \quad \begin{array}{c} 14 \\ -7 \\ \hline \end{array}$$

$$\begin{array}{c} 15 \\ -7 \\ \hline \end{array} \quad \begin{array}{c} 15 \\ -8 \\ \hline \end{array} \quad \begin{array}{c} 16 \\ -8 \\ \hline \end{array} \quad \begin{array}{c} 17 \\ -9 \\ \hline \end{array} \quad \begin{array}{c} 17 \\ -8 \\ \hline \end{array} \quad \begin{array}{c} 18 \\ -9 \\ \hline \end{array}$$

- When finished, children should find a partner and use their flash cards to practice using doubles to subtract.

- After practicing the doubles subtraction facts at school, children may continue practice at home, recording practice minutes and returning the completed record to school to be exchanged for a certificate.

Tips

If children initially have difficulty with a mixed set of flash cards, separate them into doubles and near doubles for several practice sessions.

Name_____ Date _____

1A BASIC FACTS

Counting

Count. Circle the number that tells how many.

1. ● ●

1   ②️   3

2. ● ● ● ●

2   3   4

3. ● ● ● ●
   ● ● ● ●

6   7   8

4. ● ● ● ●
   ● ● ● ●

10   11   12

5. ● ● ●
   ● ● ●

4   5   6

6. ● ● ●
   ● ● ● ●

5   6   7

7. ● ● ●

3   4   5

8. ● ● ● ● ●

4   5   6

Name_____   Date _____

1B BASIC FACTS

Counting

Draw dots. Show how many.

1. 8 	2. 6
3. 7	4. 9
5. 4	6. 5
7. 2	8. 3

Name_____   Date _____

2A ◣ BASIC FACTS

The Ten-Frame Model

Ring the number.

1.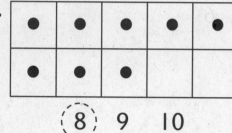

    (8) 9 10

2.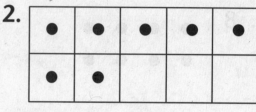

    7 8 9

3.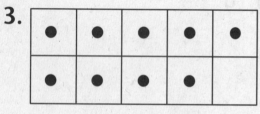

    8 9 10

4.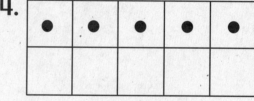

    4 5 6

5.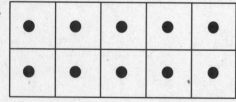

    8 9 10

6.

    3 4 5

7.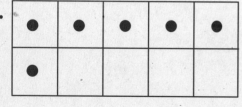

    5 6 7

8.

    7 8 9

Name_____   Date _____

2B BASIC FACTS

....

The Ten-Frame Model

Write the number.

1.

-10-

2.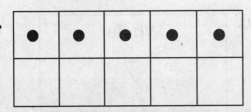

3.

4.

5.

6.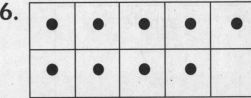

7.

8.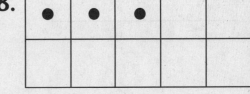

Name_____ Date _____

3A ◣ BASIC FACTS

Part-Part-Whole Model

Draw dots to show 7. Complete the number sentence.

1.

Whole
7

Part	Part
● ● ● ●	● ● ●

__4__ + __3__ = 7

2.

Whole
7

Part	Part

____ + ____ = 7

3.

Whole
7

Part	Part

____ + ____ = 7

4.

Whole
7

Part	Part

____ + ____ = 7

Name_____ Date _____

3B BASIC FACTS

Part-Part-Whole Model

Write the number sentence.

1.

Whole
6

Part	Part
● ● ● ●	● ●

$$\underline{4} + \underline{2} = \underline{6}$$

2.

Whole
4

Part	Part
● ●	● ●

$$\underline{\quad} + \underline{\quad} = \underline{\quad}$$

3.

Whole
5

Part	Part
● ● ●	● ●

$$\underline{\quad} + \underline{\quad} = \underline{\quad}$$

4.

Whole
3

Part	Part
● ●	●

$$\underline{\quad} + \underline{\quad} = \underline{\quad}$$

Name_____ Date _____

4A BASIC FACTS

....

Part-Part-Whole Model

Use a workmat and counters. Find the whole.
Write the number sentence.

1.

Whole
9

Part	Part
8	1

_8_ + _1_ = _9_

2.

Whole

Part	Part
5	4

____ + ____ = ____

3.

Whole

Part	Part
7	2

____ + ____ = ____

4.

Whole

Part	Part
6	3

____ + ____ = ____

Name_____   Date _____

4B BASIC FACTS

Part-Part-Whole Model

Use a workmat and counters. Find the sum.
Write the numbers.

1.

Whole
10

Part	Part
5	5

$5 + 5 = \underline{10}$

2.

Whole

Part	Part

$6 + 4 = \underline{\hspace{1cm}}$

3.

Whole

Part	Part

$10 + 0 = \underline{\hspace{1cm}}$

4.

Whole

Part	Part

$7 + 3 = \underline{\hspace{1cm}}$

Name_____ Date _____

5A ◤ BASIC FACTS

Exploring Zero

Draw dots. Write the sum.

1.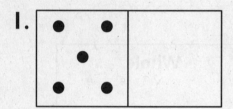

   $5 + 0 = \underline{5}$

2.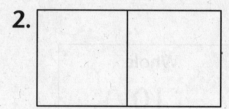

   $7 + 0 = \underline{}$

3.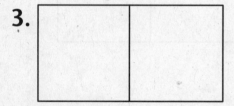

   $9 + 0 = \underline{}$

4.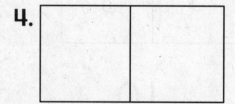

   $6 + 0 = \underline{}$

5.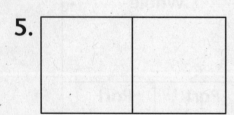

   $4 + 0 = \underline{}$

6.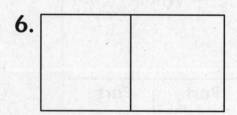

   $8 + 0 = \underline{}$

Name_____ Date _____

5B ◢ BASIC FACTS
Exploring Zero

Subtract.

1. $6 - 0 = \underline{6}$ 2. $5 - 0 = \underline{}$ 3. $8 - 8 = \underline{}$

4. $1 - 0 = \underline{}$ 5. $2 - 2 = \underline{}$ 6. $9 - 0 = \underline{}$

7. $3 - 3 = \underline{}$ 8. $7 - 0 = \underline{}$ 9. $4 - 0 = \underline{}$

10. $\begin{array}{r} 7 \\ -\,0 \\ \hline \end{array}$ 11. $\begin{array}{r} 1 \\ -\,1 \\ \hline \end{array}$ 12. $\begin{array}{r} 7 \\ -\,7 \\ \hline \end{array}$ 13. $\begin{array}{r} 3 \\ -\,0 \\ \hline \end{array}$

14. $\begin{array}{r} 9 \\ -\,9 \\ \hline \end{array}$ 15. $\begin{array}{r} 8 \\ -\,0 \\ \hline \end{array}$ 16. $\begin{array}{r} 5 \\ -\,5 \\ \hline \end{array}$ 17. $\begin{array}{r} 6 \\ -\,6 \\ \hline \end{array}$

18. $\begin{array}{r} 2 \\ -\,2 \\ \hline \end{array}$ 19. $\begin{array}{r} 9 \\ -\,0 \\ \hline \end{array}$ 20. $\begin{array}{r} 1 \\ -\,0 \\ \hline \end{array}$ 21. $\begin{array}{r} 2 \\ -\,0 \\ \hline \end{array}$

Name_____ Date _____

6A BASIC FACTS

Double Ten-Frames

Write the number.

1.
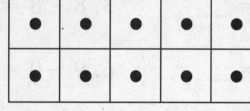

14

2.

_ _ _ _ _ _ _ _

3.

_ _ _ _ _ _ _ _

4.

_ _ _ _ _ _ _ _

Name_____ Date _____

6B BASIC FACTS
Double Ten-Frames

Write a matching number sentence.

1.

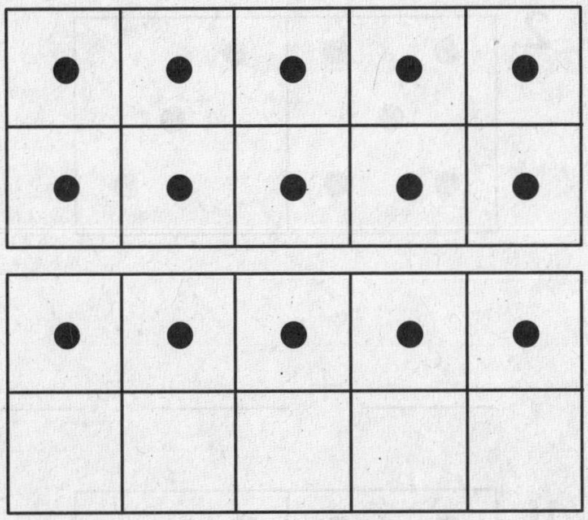

$$10 + 5 = 15$$

2.

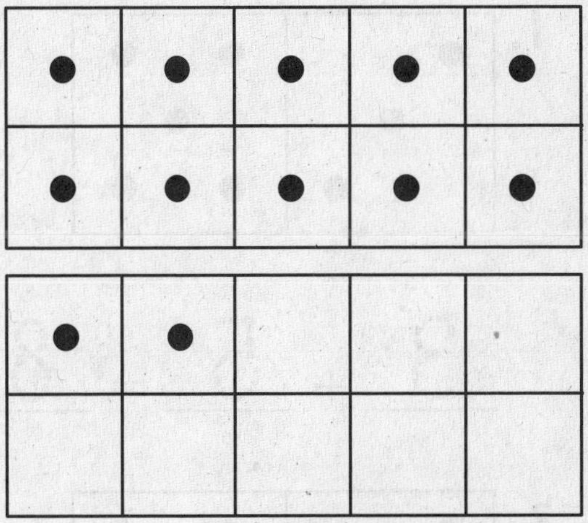

_____

3.

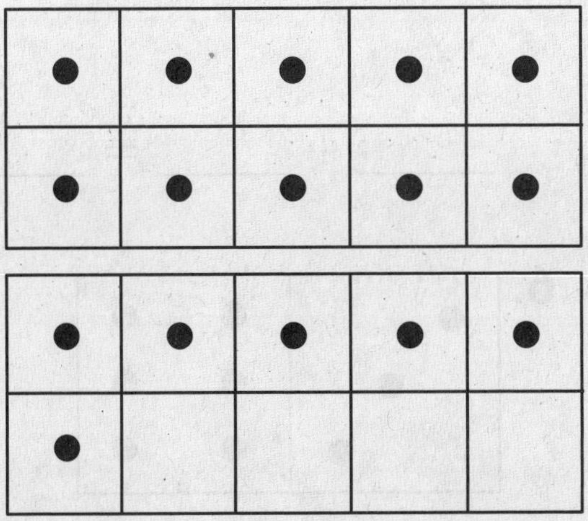

_____

4.

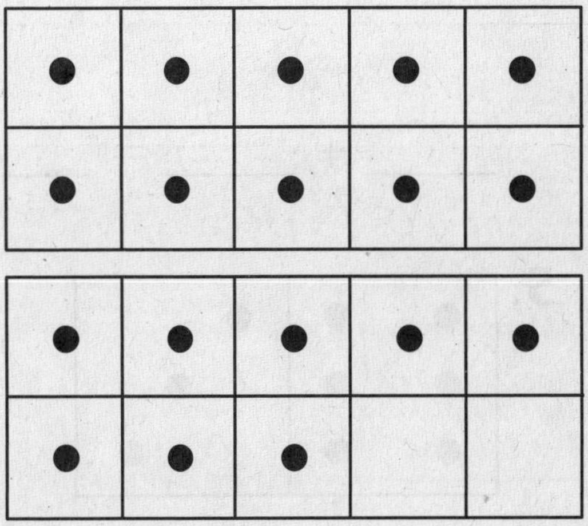

_____

Name_____ Date _____

7A ▶ BASIC FACTS

Order Property

Write a number sentence to match.

1.

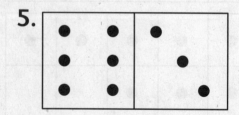

_3_ + _5_ = _8_

2.

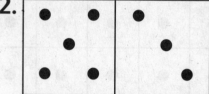

____ + ____ = ____

3.

____ + ____ = ____

4.

____ + ____ = ____

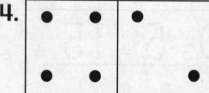

5.

____ + ____ = ____

6.

____ + ____ = ____

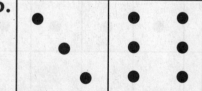

Name_____ Date _____

7B BASIC FACTS

··

Order Property

Think of order. Add.

1. 1   3
   +3   +1
    4   4

2. 1   4
   +4   +1

3. 5   1
   +1   +5

4. 2   3
   +3   +2

5. 6   3
   +3   +6

6. 2   4
   +4   +2

7. 3   4
   +4   +3

8. 3   7
   +7   +3

9. 5   3
   +3   +5

10. 6   2
   +2   +6

11. 2   5
   +5   +2

12. 2   7
   +7   +2

Name_____ Date _____

8A BASIC FACTS

Counting On to Add

Count on. Write the sum. Use the dots to help.

1. 3
   $+ 3$ • • •
    6

2. 7
   $+ 1$ •

3. 5
   $+ 2$ • •

4. 1
   $+ 1$ •

5. 6
   $+ 2$ • •

6. 8
   $+ 1$ •

7. 9
   $+ 2$ • •

8. 5
   $+ 1$ •

9. 3
   $+ 2$ • •

10. 3
   $+ 1$ •

11. 7
   $+ 2$ • •

12. 9
   $+ 1$ •

13. 2
   $+ 2$ • •

14. 6
   $+ 1$ •

15. 4
   $+ 2$ • •

16. 8
   $+ 2$ • •

17. 4
   $+ 3$ • • •

18. 5
   $+ 3$ • • •

19. 1
   $+ 2$ • •

20. 6
   $+ 3$ • • •

Name_____ Date _____

8B BASIC FACTS

Counting On to Add

Circle the greater number. Count on. Write the sum.

1. (4) + 1 = 5   2. 3 + 5 = ___   3. 2 + 9 = ___

4. 6 + 3 = ___   5. 3 + 4 = ___   6. 7 + 3 = ___

7. 5 + 3 = ___   8. 3 + 6 = ___   9. 8 + 3 = ___

10.   3
    + 1

11.   1
    + 9

12.   7
    + 2

13.   9
    + 3

14.   1
    + 8

15.   6
    + 1

16.   1
    + 5

17.   1
    + 7

18.   6
    + 2

19.   2
    + 8

20.   2
    + 3

21.   5
    + 1

Name_____   Date _____

9A BASIC FACTS

Counting Back to Subtract

Count back. Write the difference.

1. 4
    − 1
    3

2. 6
    − 3

3. 8
    − 1

4. 5
    − 1

5. 9
    − 2

6. 3
    − 1

7. 12
    − 3

8. 7
    − 3

9. 4
    − 2

10. 6
    − 1

11. 8
    − 2

12. 5
    − 2

13. 2
    − 1

14. 11
    − 2

15. 3
    − 2

16. 7
    − 2

17. 5
    − 3

18. 7
    − 1

19. 10
    − 3

20. 4
    − 3

Name_____   Date _____

9B BASIC FACTS
Counting Back to Subtract

Count back to subtract. Write the difference.

1. $5 - 3 =$ _2_   2. $9 - 3 =$ ___   3. $7 - 3 =$ ___

4. $5 - 2 =$ ___   5. $6 - 2 =$ ___   6. $8 - 1 =$ ___

7. $9 - 1 =$ ___   8. $7 - 2 =$ ___   9. $8 - 3 =$ ___

10. $6 - 3 =$ ___   11. $9 - 2 =$ ___   12. $5 - 1 =$ ___

13. $8 - 2 =$ ___   14. $4 - 2 =$ ___   15. $3 - 1 =$ ___

16. $\begin{array}{r} 2 \\ -1 \\ \hline \end{array}$ 17. $\begin{array}{r} 8 \\ -3 \\ \hline \end{array}$ 18. $\begin{array}{r} 7 \\ -1 \\ \hline \end{array}$ 19. $\begin{array}{r} 6 \\ -2 \\ \hline \end{array}$

20. $\begin{array}{r} 4 \\ -1 \\ \hline \end{array}$ 21. $\begin{array}{r} 6 \\ -1 \\ \hline \end{array}$ 22. $\begin{array}{r} 4 \\ -2 \\ \hline \end{array}$ 23. $\begin{array}{r} 5 \\ -3 \\ \hline \end{array}$

Name_____   Date _____

10A ◣ BASIC FACTS

Counting Up to Subtract

Count up to subtract. Write the difference.

1. 6
  − 5

2. 8
  − 7

3. 10
  − 9

4. 5
  − 4

5. 8
  − 5

6. 11
  − 9

7. 9
  − 8

8. 7
  − 5

9. 10
  − 8

10. 6
  − 4

11. 7
  − 4

12. 3
  − 2

13. 7
  − 6

14. 11
  − 8

15. 8
  − 6

16. 9
  − 7

17. 4
  − 3

18. 5
  − 3

19. 3
  − 2

20. 12
  − 9

Name_____ Date _____

10B BASIC FACTS

Counting Up to Subtract

Subtract. Write the difference. Circle the facts you count up.

1. $8 - 7 =$ ___   **2.** $7 - 2 =$ ___   **3.** $5 - 4 =$ ___

4. $7 - 4 =$ ___   **5.** $6 - 2 =$ ___   **6.** $3 - 2 =$ ___

7. $8 - 3 =$ ___   **8.** $6 - 3 =$ ___   **9.** $8 - 1 =$ ___

Subtract.

10. $\begin{array}{r} 10 \\ -\ 7 \\ \hline \end{array}$ **11.** $\begin{array}{r} 8 \\ -\ 6 \\ \hline \end{array}$ **12.** $\begin{array}{r} 9 \\ -\ 8 \\ \hline \end{array}$ **13.** $\begin{array}{r} 6 \\ -\ 4 \\ \hline \end{array}$

14. $\begin{array}{r} 10 \\ -\ 9 \\ \hline \end{array}$ **15.** $\begin{array}{r} 7 \\ -\ 5 \\ \hline \end{array}$ **16.** $\begin{array}{r} 5 \\ -\ 2 \\ \hline \end{array}$ **17.** $\begin{array}{r} 8 \\ -\ 7 \\ \hline \end{array}$

18. $\begin{array}{r} 9 \\ -\ 7 \\ \hline \end{array}$ **19.** $\begin{array}{r} 10 \\ -\ 8 \\ \hline \end{array}$ **20.** $\begin{array}{r} 12 \\ -\ 9 \\ \hline \end{array}$ **21.** $\begin{array}{r} 7 \\ -\ 3 \\ \hline \end{array}$

Name_____ Date _____

11A ◢ BASIC FACTS

Using Doubles to Add

Draw dots to show a double. Complete the number sentence.

1.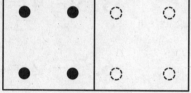

   4 + __4__ = __8__

2.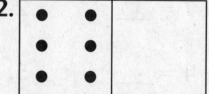

   6 + _____ = _____

3.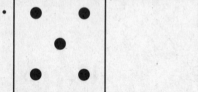

   5 + _____ = _____

4.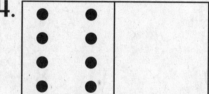

   8 + _____ = _____

5. 7
   +7

6. 9
   +9

7. 8
   +8

8. 6
   +6

Name_____ Date _____

11B BASIC FACTS

Using Doubles to Add

Find the sum of the double. Use the double to find the next sums.

1. 4   →   4   5
   + 4   →   + 5   + 4
   ___   ___   ___
    8   9   9

2. 5   →   5   6
   + 5   →   + 6   + 5
   ___   ___   ___

3. 6   →   6   7
   + 6   →   + 7   + 6
   ___   ___   ___

4. 7   →   7   8
   + 7   →   + 8   + 7
   ___   ___   ___

5. 8   →   8   9
   + 8   →   + 9   + 8
   ___   ___   ___

Name_____   Date _____

12A ▸ BASIC FACTS

Using Doubles to Subtract

Use doubles and near doubles. Subtract.

1. $8 - 4 =$ __4__   2. $10 - 5 =$ ____   3. $9 - 5 =$ ____

4. $12 - 6 =$ ____   5. $13 - 7 =$ ____   6. $11 - 6 =$ ____

7. $\begin{array}{r} 13 \\ -7 \\ \hline \end{array}$ 8. $\begin{array}{r} 14 \\ -7 \\ \hline \end{array}$ 9. $\begin{array}{r} 16 \\ -8 \\ \hline \end{array}$ 10. $\begin{array}{r} 13 \\ -6 \\ \hline \end{array}$

11. $\begin{array}{r} 16 \\ -7 \\ \hline \end{array}$ 12. $\begin{array}{r} 18 \\ -9 \\ \hline \end{array}$ 13. $\begin{array}{r} 14 \\ -8 \\ \hline \end{array}$ 14. $\begin{array}{r} 17 \\ -8 \\ \hline \end{array}$

15. $\begin{array}{r} 15 \\ -7 \\ \hline \end{array}$ 16. $\begin{array}{r} 9 \\ -4 \\ \hline \end{array}$ 17. $\begin{array}{r} 15 \\ -7 \\ \hline \end{array}$ 18. $\begin{array}{r} 12 \\ -6 \\ \hline \end{array}$

19. $\begin{array}{r} 17 \\ -9 \\ \hline \end{array}$ 20. $\begin{array}{r} 14 \\ -7 \\ \hline \end{array}$ 21. $\begin{array}{r} 15 \\ -8 \\ \hline \end{array}$ 22. $\begin{array}{r} 8 \\ -4 \\ \hline \end{array}$

Name_____ Date _____

12B BASIC FACTS

Using Doubles to Subtract

Use doubles and near doubles. Subtract.

1. $14 - 7 = \underline{7}$ 2. $11 - 6 = \underline{}$ 3. $12 - 6 = \underline{}$

4. $11 - 5 = \underline{}$ 5. $15 - 8 = \underline{}$ 6. $17 - 9 = \underline{}$

7. $15 - 7 = \underline{}$ 8. $14 - 8 = \underline{}$ 9. $17 - 8 = \underline{}$

10. $\begin{array}{r} 9 \\ -4 \\ \hline \end{array}$ 11. $\begin{array}{r} 9 \\ -5 \\ \hline \end{array}$ 12. $\begin{array}{r} 13 \\ -6 \\ \hline \end{array}$ 13. $\begin{array}{r} 13 \\ -7 \\ \hline \end{array}$

14. $\begin{array}{r} 12 \\ -6 \\ \hline \end{array}$ 15. $\begin{array}{r} 7 \\ -4 \\ \hline \end{array}$ 16. $\begin{array}{r} 15 \\ -8 \\ \hline \end{array}$ 17. $\begin{array}{r} 16 \\ -7 \\ \hline \end{array}$

18. $\begin{array}{r} 10 \\ -5 \\ \hline \end{array}$ 19. $\begin{array}{r} 16 \\ -8 \\ \hline \end{array}$ 20. $\begin{array}{r} 8 \\ -4 \\ \hline \end{array}$ 21. $\begin{array}{r} 18 \\ -9 \\ \hline \end{array}$

Basic Facts Workshop 1

Strategy: Adding and Subtracting Zero

 Introduce It!

 15 minutes

Adding Zero

Management whole class
Materials two envelopes, 9 counters

- Ask two children to come to the front of the room. Give each child an envelope, one with nine counters and the other one with none.

- Ask the class to find the total number of counters in both envelopes.

- Open the envelope with counters, and have children count them. Write 9 on the chalkboard.

- Open the other envelope and ask, How many counters are in this envelope? **none** How many counters are there in all? **9**

- Write the addition sentence $9 + 0 = 9$ on the chalkboard.

- Have the children change places. Ask the class to identify the number of counters in the envelopes (0 and 9). How would you write an addition sentence for this? $0 + 9 = 9$ Repeat with other examples, adding zero.

- Change the number of counters in one envelope and always leave the other envelope empty.

- Ask three volunteers to repeat the activity. Two children report what's in the envelopes, and the third child writes the addition sentences on the chalkboard.

- Repeat with other children.

 Develop It!

 15 minutes

Subtracting All or None

Management whole class
Materials overhead projector, blank transparency, 9 counters

- Show 7 counters on the overhead projector. Ask children how many they see.

- Ask children to close their eyes. Remove all 7 counters.

- Have children open their eyes and describe what happened.

- Ask the class how to write a number sentence that shows what you just did. Guide them to write $7 - 7 = 0$.

- Repeat with eight counters. Ask children how many they see.

- Have children close their eyes. Do not remove any counters.

- Ask children to open their eyes and describe what happened.

- Ask the class how to write a number sentence that shows what you just did. Guide them to write $8 - 8 = 0$.

- Repeat activity asking one child to put counters on the projector and the other child to record the number sentence.

- Repeat with other children.

Make It!

Make Zero Flash Cards

20 minutes

Management individuals

Materials 10 triangle-shaped cards (Achieving Facts Fluency Support Master 4), 2 different-colored markers, large envelope to store triangle flash cards, practice minutes record and certificate (Achieving Facts Fluency Support Masters 9 and 13)

- Have each child cut ten triangle-shaped flash cards from Support Master 4 and make flash cards as shown.

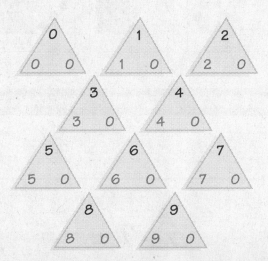

- To use triangle-shaped flash cards, one child holds a card and covers a corner. If the two numbers are the same color, then two addition facts can be stated. If the two numbers are different colors, the subtraction fact is stated.

- Have children work with a partner and practice adding and subtracting with zero. Encourage children to continue at home and record practice using the practice minutes record. The completed record may be returned to school and exchanged for a certificate.

Tips

Remind children that these flash cards will be used all year, so they should put their initials on the back of each card.

Basic Facts Workshop 2

Strategy: Counting On 1, 2, 3 to Add

Introduce It!

15 minutes

Counting On 1, 2, 3

Management whole class
Materials overhead projector, 12 counters

- Show 7 counters on the projector. Ask children how many they see. **7** Cover the counters with a piece of paper. Place two counters beside the paper. Ask, How many more counters do you see? **2** How many counters are there in all? **9** How do you know? Write 7 + 2 = 9

- Repeat with other sets of counters, 5, 6, and 8. Always add 1, 2, or 3 more counters. Write number sentences for each example.

- Reverse the order of addends. Show 6 counters on the right side of the projector, cover them, and place 3 counters to the left of the paper. Ask, How many are there in all? **9**

- Write 3 + 6 = 9. Ask, How is the number sentence different? **Addends have changed position.** Did you count on to find the sum? How? **Remembered 6, then counted on, 7, 8, 9.**

$7 + 2 = 9$

$3 + 6 = 9$

Develop It!

20 minutes

Start with the Greater Number

Management whole class
Materials overhead projector, blank transparency

- Write 3 + 7 = on a transparency. Ask the class, How can you use counting on to find the sum? **Possible answer: Think 7, then count 8, 9, 10.** Could you also start at 3 and count on 7 more? Which way is easier? Why?

- Lead children to see that it is easier to start with the greater addend.

$3 + 7 =$

Tips
Have children use their fingers to help them count on.

Make It!

Make Counting On
Flash Cards

20 minutes

Management individuals
Materials 45 white index cards, storage container for cards, practice minutes record and certificate (Achieving Facts Fluency Support Masters 9 and 13)

- Distribute 45 white index cards to each child. Remind children to write addends only on the front of the card, and addends and sum on the back of each card. They may want to write their initials or names on the back of each card also.

- Have children make a separate flash card for each of the facts shown.

- When finished, children should find a partner and use their flash cards to practice adding by counting on.

- After practicing at school, children may continue their practice at home, recording practice minutes and returning the completed record to school to exchange for a certificate.

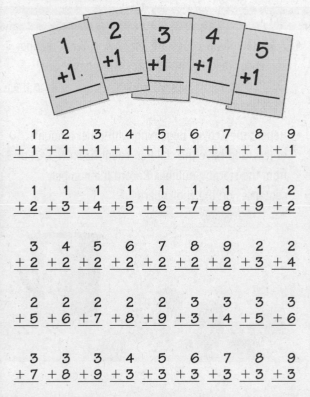

1	2	3	4	5	6	7	8	9
+ 1	+ 1	+ 1	+ 1	+ 1	+ 1	+ 1	+ 1	+ 1

1	1	1	1	1	1	1	1	2
+ 2	+ 3	+ 4	+ 5	+ 6	+ 7	+ 8	+ 9	+ 2

3	4	5	6	7	8	9	2	2
+ 2	+ 2	+ 2	+ 2	+ 2	+ 2	+ 2	+ 3	+ 4

2	2	2	2	2	3	3	3	3
+ 5	+ 6	+ 7	+ 8	+ 9	+ 3	+ 4	+ 5	+ 6

3	3	3	4	5	6	7	8	9
+ 7	+ 8	+ 9	+ 3	+ 3	+ 3	+ 3	+ 3	+ 3

Basic Facts Workshop 3

Strategy: Counting Back

Introduce It!

15 minutes

Counting Back

Management whole class
Materials none

- First invite ten children to come to the front of the room and stand in a line. Ask, How many children do you see? **10** Then ask two children to kneel down and talk about how to write what happened. Then write 10 − 2 on the chalkboard.

- Ask the class how many are left standing. To find out, start at 10 and count back 2. Encourage them to think 10, and then count 9, 8. Ask, How would you finish the number sentence? Guide children to suggest writing 8 after the equal sign.

- Repeat the activity with 9 children. Have 3 sit down. Record the number sentence, thinking aloud to demonstrate counting back 3. Then repeat with 7 − 2, 5 − 2, and 8 − 3.

Tips

Use a number line to demonstrate, so that children can see the numbers while they count back.

Develop It!

20 minutes

Count Back and Keep Track

Management whole class
Materials 10 connecting cubes, container

- Place 7 cubes in your hand. Show them to the children and ask how many they see.

- Take out 3, and one at a time, drop them into a container.

- Ask children to think 7 and then count back 6, 5, 4. as they hear each cube clink.

- Ask, How many cubes are left? **4** Ask, What number sentence could I write to show what happened? Guide children to suggest writing 7 − 3 = 4 on the chalkboard.

- Repeat the activity beginning with other amounts, 10 or less, and have the children count back by 1, 2, or 3 from the starting number. Record the number sentences on the chalkboard.

Make It!

Counting Back Flash Cards

20 minutes

Management individuals or pairs
Materials 22 index cards, practice minutes record and certificate (Achieving Facts Fluency Support Masters 10 and 14)

- Distribute index cards to each child. Remind children to write their initials or names on the back of each.

- Then ask children to make flash cards as shown.

$$
\begin{array}{cccccccccc}
2 & 3 & 4 & 5 & 6 & 8 & 9 & 3 & 8 \\
-1 & -1 & -1 & -1 & -1 & -1 & -1 & -2 & -3
\end{array}
$$

$$
\begin{array}{cccccccccc}
4 & 5 & 6 & 8 & 9 & 4 & 5 & 6 & 9 \\
-2 & -2 & -2 & -2 & -2 & -3 & -3 & -3 & -3
\end{array}
$$

- Invite children to use their flash cards with a partner to practice subtracting by counting back.

- Encourage children to combine these flash cards with their counting on flash cards, and continue to practice at home. Have them record their practice minutes and return the completed record to school to be exchanged for a certificate.

Tips

Remind children to write the expression only on the front of each card and the complete number sentence on the back.

Basic Facts Workshop 4

Strategy: Counting Up

Introduce It!

15 minutes

Counting Up

Management whole class
Materials overhead projector, part-part-whole mat transparency (Achieving Facts Fluency Support Master 2), large index cards, 10 counters

- Place 7 counters on the whole part of the part-part-whole transparency.

- Ask the children how many they see. Remove the counters and write 7. Slide 5 counters to one part of the mat, slide 2 to the other part, keeping those two covered with a card.

- Ask children how many counters they started with, **7** how many counters are in the part they know, **5** and how many counters they think are in the other part. One way to find out is to count up. Say, Start with 5, count up to 7. Think 6, 7. How many do you count up? **2** Write $7 - 5 = 2$.

- Repeat the activity for other subtraction situations such as $9 - 6$, $8 - 6$, $6 - 5$, and $7 - 4$.

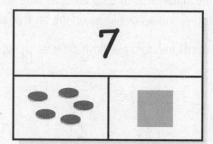

Develop It!

15 minutes

Count Up Flash

Management pairs
Materials 3 index cards labeled numbers 1, 2, and 3

- Write $8 - 5$ on the chalkboard.

- Remind children that counting up is a good subtraction strategy to use when numbers are close together.

- Pairs share their answers and hold up the 1, 2, or 3 card. Discuss the correct answer.

- Repeat with the following, $9 - 7$, $10 - 7$, $11 - 8$, $7 - 6$, $7 - 5$, $9 - 6$, $7 - 4$, $9 - 8$, $8 - 6$, and $7 - 6$. Pairs take turns holding up the appropriate card.

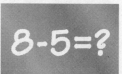

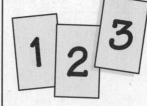

Make It!

Make Counting Up Flash Cards

20 minutes

Management individuals

Materials 18 orange-colored index cards, storage container for flash cards, practice minutes record and certificate (Achieving Facts Fluency Support Masters 9 and 13)

- Distribute 18 orange-colored index cards to each child.

- Remind children to write the expression only on the front of the card, and the complete number sentence on the back. Also ask children to write their names or initials on the back of each card.

- Have children make a separate flash card for each fact as shown below.

```
12    11    10
-9    -8    -7     7     5
                  -5    -4
```

```
11    10    10     9     9     9
-9    -9    -8    -8    -7    -6
```

```
8     8     8     7     7     6     6
-7    -6    -5    -6    -4    -5    -4
```

- When finished, children should find a partner and use their flash cards to practice. After practicing at school, children may continue practice at home, recording practice minutes, and returning the completed record to school to be exchanged for a certificate.

Tips

You many want to laminate flash cards so they will last throughout the year.

Basic Facts Workshop 5
Strategy Review

Introduce It!

15 minutes

Choose a Strategy

Management whole class
Materials none

- Write 9 + 2 on the chalkboard. Ask, If you can't remember the answer for 9 + 2, how could you figure it out? **Count on from 9.** Would that work for 3 + 7? **Yes, start with 7, count on 3.**

- Then, write 12 − 3 on the chalkboard. Ask, How could you figure out the answer if you can't remember it? **Start with 12, count back 3.**

- Next, write the following on the chalkboard: 7 + 2, 9 + 3, 8 − 3, 11 + 3, 10 − 2, 15 − 3, and 12 + 1. Ask children to describe how to solve each example by counting on or counting back.

- Finally, write 12 − 9. Ask, Should I count back to find the answer? **No, it would be hard to keep track.** How should I solve the problem? **Start at 9 and count up.**

- Have children count up to find 10 − 8, 13 − 10, 9 − 7, 12 − 10, and 8 − 5.

Tips

Remind children that it is easier to count on when you add 1, 2, or 3; and count back with greater numbers.

Develop It!

15 minutes

Show a Strategy

Management pairs
Materials two different colors of chalk

- Divide children into pairs and have them talk about how they know when to count on, count back, and count up. Ask them to share their ideas with examples. Record their examples on the chalkboard.

- Next, draw a triangle on the chalkboard, with the number 9 at the top in one color of chalk, and the numbers 2 and 7 at the bottom in another color. Cover the 9, reminding children that since they know the two parts, they can add them. Ask children how

they can figure out 2 + 7 and 7 + 2 if they can't remember them. Write 2 + 7 = 9 and 7 + 2 = 9 underneath the triangle.

- Next, cover the 2, reminding children that since they know the whole and one part, they subtract. Ask how to figure out 9 − 7. Write 9 − 7 = 2. Cover the 7. Ask them how to figure out 9 − 2. Write 9 − 2 = 7.

- Repeat the activity with other numbers.

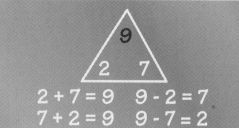

Make It!

20 minutes

Make Triangle Cards

Management individuals or pairs

Materials 24 triangle flash cards (Achieving Facts Fluency
Support Master 4), previously made triangle flash cards, practice
minutes record and certificate (Achieving Facts Fluency Support
Masters 11 and 15), two different colored markers

- Have each child cut 24 triangle flash cards from copies
  of Achieving Facts Fluency Support Master 4. Remind
  them to write their initials or first names on the back.

- Children can label flash cards as shown. Tell them to
  write the top number in one color and the bottom
  two in the second color.

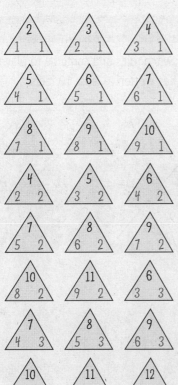

- When finished, divide children into pairs to practice
  the counting on, counting back, and counting up
  facts.

- After reviewing these facts at school, children may
  add in the zero triangle flash cards and practice with
  them at home. Children should record the time spent
  working at home on Support Master 11. When they
  come back to school, the record can be exchanged
  for a certificate.

Basic Facts Workshop 6

Strategy: Using Doubles to Add

Introduce It!

20 minutes

Where Is the Double?

Management whole class
Materials overhead projector, teacher-made transparency of part-part-whole mat (Achieving Facts Fluency Support Master 2), counters

- Place five counters on one part of the part-part-whole mat. Ask, How many counters should go on the other part to show a double? **5** How many counters are there now? **5 + 5 = 10**

- Place one more counter on one side of the workmat. Ask, How does knowing 5 + 5 help you figure out 5 + 6? **one more than 10; 5 + 6 = 11**

- Then, write 8 + 7. Ask, What double helps with this fact? **7 + 7 and one more, or one less than 8 + 8** Ask a child to model with counters.

- Have children take turns modeling with counters and identifying a helping double for each of the following expressions: 4 + 5, 5 + 7, 7 + 9, 9 + 8, and 6 + 8.

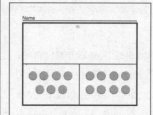

Develop It!

20 minutes

Spin and Double

Management pairs
Materials 2 spinners (Achieving Facts Fluency Support Masters 5 and 6)

- Distribute to each pair a 6-section spinner labeled, 4, 5, 6, 7, 8, and 9; and a 3-section spinner labeled, double, double + 1, and double + 2.

- First, one partner spins the 6-section spinner to determine a number, and then the 3-section spinner to determine what to do with that number.

- The other partner records the addition fact. For example, if the number spun is 6 and the direction is double + 2, the fact to record is 6 + 8 = 14.

- Players switch roles and continue to play until each partner has written at least 10 facts.

Tips

Write out the possible facts so that children can refer to them when they play.

25 minutes

Make Doubles, Near Doubles Flash Cards

Management individuals

Materials 24 blue index cards, practice minutes record and certificate (Achieving Facts Fluency Support Masters 9 and 13)

- Write a double or near double addition problem on each of sixteen flash cards as shown and display them on the ledge of the chalkboard. Distribute sixteen blue index cards to each child.

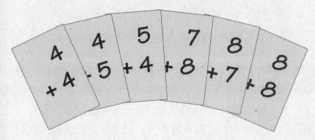

$$\begin{array}{r} 4 \\ +4 \end{array} \quad \begin{array}{r} 4 \\ +5 \end{array} \quad \begin{array}{r} 5 \\ +4 \end{array} \quad \begin{array}{r} 7 \\ +8 \end{array} \quad \begin{array}{r} 8 \\ +7 \end{array} \quad \begin{array}{r} 8 \\ +8 \end{array}$$

$$\begin{array}{r} 4 \\ +6 \end{array} \quad \begin{array}{r} 5 \\ +5 \end{array} \quad \begin{array}{r} 5 \\ +6 \end{array} \quad \begin{array}{r} 5 \\ +7 \end{array} \quad \begin{array}{r} 6 \\ +4 \end{array} \quad \begin{array}{r} 6 \\ +5 \end{array} \quad \begin{array}{r} 6 \\ +6 \end{array} \quad \begin{array}{r} 6 \\ +7 \end{array} \quad \begin{array}{r} 6 \\ +8 \end{array}$$

$$\begin{array}{r} 7 \\ +5 \end{array} \quad \begin{array}{r} 7 \\ +6 \end{array} \quad \begin{array}{r} 7 \\ +7 \end{array} \quad \begin{array}{r} 7 \\ +9 \end{array} \quad \begin{array}{r} 8 \\ +6 \end{array} \quad \begin{array}{r} 8 \\ +9 \end{array} \quad \begin{array}{r} 9 \\ +7 \end{array} \quad \begin{array}{r} 9 \\ +8 \end{array} \quad \begin{array}{r} 9 \\ +9 \end{array}$$

- Ask children to copy one addition problem on the front of each card and write the sum on the back of the card. Have children also write their names on the back of each card.

- Then, ask children to use their flash cards to quiz a partner on adding doubles and near doubles.

- After practicing at school, children may bring their flash cards home to practice. Tell children to record the minutes practiced and return the completed record to school to be exchanged for a certificate.

Basic Facts Workshop 7

Strategy: Using Doubles to Subtract

Introduce It!

15 minutes

The Missing Part

> **Management** whole class
> **Materials** 17 counters

- Show 9 counters to children. Ask, How many counters do you see?

- Put all 9 counters in your pocket. Take out 4 counters and show them. Write $9 - 4 =$ ___ on the chalkboard.

- Ask, How many do you think are still in my pocket? Could it be 4? **no** Why? **4 and 4 are only 8, you need one more, or 5, to make 9** Write $9 - 4 = 5$.

- Draw and label a part-part-whole diagram below the number sentence. Ask children how using doubles can help them find the missing part ($4 + 4 = 8$, so $4 + 5 = 9$, so $9 - 4 = 5$).

- Repeat with 15 counters in your pocket and remove 7; 17 in the pocket and remove 9; and 13 in the pocket and remove 6. Emphasize thinking about doubles to find the missing part.

Tips

Emphasize that with doubles, the two parts on the part-part-whole diagram will be the same.

Develop It!

15 minutes

Name the Doubles

> **Management** whole class
> **Materials** none

- Write $15 - 8 =$ ___ on the chalkboard. Ask, How can you use doubles to help solve this problem? ($8 + 8$

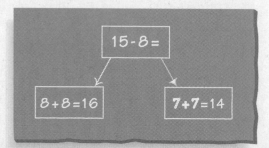

$= 16$, so $8 + 7 = 15$, so $15 - 8$ must be 7; or $7 + 7 = 14$, so $7 + 8 = 15$, so $15 - 8$ must be 7.)

- Repeat with the following examples:

  $13 - 7$; $17 - 9$; $15 - 7$; $17 - 8$; and $13 - 6$.

- Ask, Can you use doubles to solve each problem? Some children may solve $13 - 7$ by thinking $7 + 7 = 14$, so $7 + 6 = 13$, so $13 - 7 = 6$, or others may think $6 + 6 = 12$, so $6 + 7 = 13$, so $13 - 7 = 6$.

Tips

Remind children that they should use the doubles that are easiest for them. Not everyone looks at a problem the same way.

Make It!

30 minutes

Make Doubles, Near Doubles Flash Cards

Management individuals

Materials 21 blue index cards, previously made set of index card flash cards, practice minutes record and certificate (Achieving Facts Fluency Support Masters 10 and 14)

- Distribute 21 blue index cards to each child.

- Have children make flash cards for the following doubles and near doubles facts:

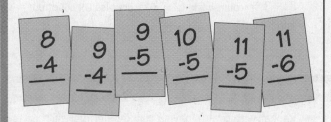

$$
\begin{array}{cccccccc}
10 & 10 & 12 & 12 & 13 & 13 & 14 & 14 \\
-4 & -6 & -5 & -6 & -7 & -6 & -6 & -7 \\
\hline
\end{array}
$$

$$
\begin{array}{ccccccc}
15 & 15 & 16 & 16 & 17 & 17 & 18 \\
-7 & -8 & -7 & -8 & -9 & -8 & -9 \\
\hline
\end{array}
$$

- When finished, children should find a partner and use their flash cards to practice using doubles to subtract.

- After practicing the doubles subtraction facts at school, children may combine these flash cards with previously made flash cards, and continue practicing at home, recording practice minutes and returning the completed record to school to be exchanged for a certificate.

Basic Facts Workshop 8
Strategy Review

Introduce It!

15 minutes

What Strategy Will Help?

Management whole class
Materials chalkboard, large self-adhesive notes

- List the following addition and subtraction strategies on the chalkboard as shown: count on, count back, count up, doubles/near doubles.

- Remind children that they have learned each of these strategies as a way to help figure out facts they don't remember. Review strategies if necessary.

- Write 7 + 2 = on a self-adhesive note. Show it to

the class and ask which strategy could help them figure out this fact if they couldn't remember it. **counting on** Place the self-adhesive note under count on on the chalkboard

count on	count back	count up	doubles/ near doubles
7+2		10-7	8+8

- Repeat, showing the following facts to the class and having them identify the strategy that would be helpful, to find the answer: $10 - 7 = $ **count up**; $8 + 8 = $ **doubles**; $9 + 3 = $ **count on**; $7 + 8 = $ **near doubles**; $8 - 3 = $ **count back**; $6 - 3 = $ **doubles OR count up**; and $11 - 3 = $ **count back**.

Develop It!

15 minutes

Name the Strategy

Management individuals
Materials none

- Have each child fold a paper into four parts and label each part as shown.

- Write 8 + 2 = on the chalkboard. Ask children which strategy they would use if they couldn't remember the answer. **counting on** Why? **You can keep the greater number in your head and count on**

- Have children write the complete number sentence **8 + 2 = 10** in the count on section of their paper.

- Repeat with 6 + 6, having children decide which strategy would be helpful. **doubles** Have them write the complete number sentence in that section, and discuss their decision.

- Repeat, using the following number sentences: 7 + 7 **doubles**, 13 − 2 **count back**, 12 − 9 **count up**, 4 + 3 **near doubles or counting on**, 8 + 9 **near doubles**, 9 − 7 **count up**, 11 − 3 **count back**, and 9 + 3 **count on**.

Make It!

15 minutes

Make Doubles
Triangle Flash Cards

Management individuals, then pairs

Materials 15 triangle-shaped flash cards (Achieving Facts Fluency Support Master 4), 2 different-colored markers, practice minutes record and certificate (Achieving Facts Fluency Support Masters 10 and 14)

- Distribute triangle-shaped flash cards (Support Master 4). Have children make flash cards like the ones shown below. Remind children to write the top number in one color, and the two bottom numbers in a second color.

- When finished, children may find a partner and use the doubles/near doubles flash cards to review addition and subtraction facts.

- After practicing the doubles/near doubles facts, children may add these flash cards to their previously made set of triangle cards and take them home to continue review. Practice minutes may be recorded and forms may be returned to school to exchange for a certificate.

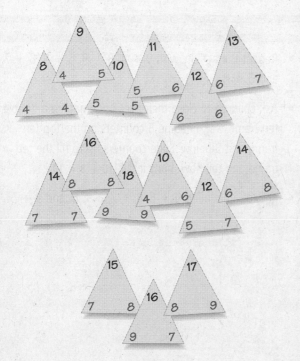

Tips

Remind children that the sum of two odd numbers or two even numbers will always be even, while the sum of an even and odd number will always be odd.

75

Basic Facts Workshop 9
Strategy: Using Ten to Add

 Introduce It!

15 minutes

Make a Ten

Management whole class
Materials overhead projector, double ten-frame workmat (Achieving Facts Fluency Support Master 3) and teacher-made double ten-frame transparency, 19 counters

- Review adding any number to ten. Have children state answers to 10 + 3, 10 + 8, 10 + 5, 10 + 6, 10 + 9, 10 + 4, 10 + 7, and 10 + 1.

- Show 8 counters on a double ten-frame transparency. Ask children how many they see? **8** Show 6 more counters in the bottom ten frame. Ask children how many more they see? **6** Write 8 + 6 = __.

- Slide 2 counters up to make a ten. Ask children to use the ten fact to find how many counters in all. **14** Write 8 + 6 = 14.

- Distribute a workmat and 20 counters to each child.

- Write the following examples on the chalkboard, having children model each with counters, move counters to make a ten, then find the answer: 9 + 7, 8 + 5, 9 + 8, 7 + 8, 9 + 6, and 8 + 7.

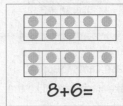

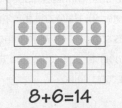

 Develop It!

20 minutes

Imagine a Ten

Management whole class
Materials chalkboard, ten-frame workmat (Achieving Facts Fluency Support Master 1)

- Have children clear their counters from their ten frames. Write 9 + 4 on the chalkboard. Tell the class to look at their workmats and imagine 9 counters on the top ten frame and 4 counters below without really placing any counters on the mat.

- Ask children to imagine sliding a counter up to fill the top frame. Ask, How many counters are there in all? **13** How did you know? **10 + 3 = 13** Write 9 + 4 = 13 on the chalkboard.

- Repeat the activity with 9 + 4, 8 + 9, 6 + 9, 8 + 7, and 6 + 8.

- Ask children to close their eyes and imagine a double ten frame. Say, Imagine 8 counters on the top ten frame and 5 below. Slide counters up to fill the ten frame and tell how many in all. **10 + 3 = 13**

- Repeat, imagining 9 + 6, 8 + 7, 8 + 6, and 9 + 5.

20 minutes

Make a Ten Flash Cards

Management individuals

Materials 20 green index cards, previously made flash cards, practice minutes record and certificate (Achieving Facts Fluency Support Masters 10 and 14)

- Distribute 20 green index cards to each child. Have children make flash cards for the following make a ten facts:

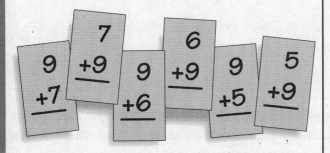

```
 9    4    8    7    8    6    8
+4   +9   +7   +8   +6   +8   +5


 5    8    4    7    5    7    4
+8   +4   +8   +5   +7   +4   +7
```

- When finished all children may use their flash cards to practice the facts with a partner.

- After practicing at school, children may continue practicing at home, recording the practice minutes and returning the completed record to school to exchange for a certificate.

Tips

Encourage children to create the flash cards in the order of the pattern so that no facts are forgotten. Remind children to write their initials on the back of each card.

Basic Facts Workshop 10
Strategy: Using Ten to Subtract

Introduce It!

15 minutes

Make a Ten

Management whole class
Materials overhead projector, ten-frame and teacher-made ten-frame transparency (Achieving Facts Fluency Support Master 1), 20 two-sided counters

- Show nine counters of one color on the top ten frame of a transparency. Write 16 − 9 at the top.

- Ask, If you know the whole is 16 and one part is 9, how might you find the other part?

- Use a second color to finish filling the top ten frame and put six counters on the second ten frame. Remind the class that to get from 9 to 16, you need one counter to make ten and another six counters to make 16.

- How many counters did you use for the second part? **7** Write = 7 after 16 − 9 at the top.

- Repeat the activity, having children use ten-frame mats to model 15 − 8, 18 − 9, 13 − 8, 14 − 9, 13 − 7, and 17 − 9. Remind children to show counters for the part they know, then use more counters to make a ten, then add more to get to the whole.

Develop It!

15 minutes

Imagine a Ten

Management whole class
Materials double ten-frame workmat (Achieving Facts Fluency Support Master 3)

- Write 14 − 8 on the chalkboard. Ask children what they know about the whole or parts in the problem. **The whole is 14 and one part is 8.** Ask, How might you find the other part? **Use counters to get from 8 to 14.**

- Tell the class to look at their ten-frame mats and think about the part they know, or eight counters, on the top frame, without really placing any counters on the mat. Ask children to think about putting more

counters on the mat to make a ten, then add more to get to 14. Ask, How many counters did you use for the second part? **6**

- Write 14 − 8 = 6 on the chalkboard. Repeat the activity with examples such as 13 − 8, 15 − 8, and 14 − 9.

- Next, ask children to turn the ten-frame mats over, and think about double ten frames in their heads. Say, If you want to find the answer to 16 − 9, imagine the 9 counters for the part you know. Now, imagine putting more counters on to get to 16. How many did you use for the other part? **7** Repeat, using 15 − 9, and 17 − 8.

Make It!

20 minutes

Make Ten to Subtract Flash Cards

Management individuals

Materials 20 green index cards, previously made flash cards, practice minutes record and certificate (Achieving Facts Fluency Support Masters 10 and 14)

• Distribute 20 green index cards to each child.

• Have children make flash cards for these facts:

$$
\begin{array}{ccccc}
14 & 14 & 15 & 15 & 15 \\
-8 & -9 & -7 & -8 & -9 \\
\end{array}
$$

$$
\begin{array}{ccccc}
16 & 16 & 16 & 17 & 17 \\
-7 & -8 & -9 & -8 & -9 \\
\end{array}
$$

• When finished, children may use the flash cards to practice making a ten to subtract with a partner.

• After practicing at school, children may continue practice at home, recording practice minutes and returning the completed record to school to exchange for a certificate.

Tips

Remind children to write their numbers large enough so the numbers can be read easily.

Basic Facts Workshop 11

Strategy: Using Ten to Subtract

Introduce It!

15 minutes

Tens Again

Management whole class

Materials overhead projector, teacher-made double ten-frame transparency, 20 overhead counters; 20 counters, double ten-frame workmat (Achieving Facts Fluency Support Master 3) per child

• Show 15 counters 10 on the top frame, and 5 counters on the bottom frame. Ask children how many they see.

• Write $15 - 6$ on the top of the transparency. Ask the class what they know about parts and whole in this problem. The whole is 15, and one part is 6. Ask, When you subtract, what do you need to find?

• Remind children that using 10 can help them to subtract 6 from 15 to find the other part. Say, First, you can take 5 away to get to ten, remove counters from the bottom frame. Then you take one more away to get to 9. Ask, What is the other part? Write $15 - 6 = 9$.

• Repeat the activity, having children use double ten-frame mats to model $13 - 4$, $11 - 4$, $14 - 6$, $13 - 5$, and $12 - 5$. Remind children to show counters for the whole, subtract some to go back to ten, then go back further to find the other part.

Develop It!

15 minutes

Imagine a Ten Again

Management whole class

Materials double ten-frame workmat (Achieving Facts Fluency Support Master 3) per child

• Write $13 - 5$ on the chalkboard. Have children look at their workmats and *imagine* 13 counters. Ask the class how using a ten could help subtract 5. **Imagine taking off 3 counters to get to ten, then two more to get 8.**

• Repeat the activity with examples such as $11 - 4$, $14 - 6$, $12 - 5$, and $13 - 4$. Remind children to imagine the whole, then use the part they know to

count back to ten and further to find the other part. Write $12 - 9$ and $12 - 4$ on the chalkboard. Remind the class that there are two ways to use a ten to subtract. They can start with the whole and use ten to help them subtract one part, or they could start with one part and count up to the whole to find the other part.

• Ask children how they would decide to use a ten to count up or count back. **If the part you know is small, counting back works best; if the part is large, counting up works best.**

• Use the following facts $15 - 9$, $14 - 9$, $12 - 4$, $13 - 5$, $12 - 8$, $13 - 4$, and $13 - 8$ to practice the using ten to subtract strategy.

Make It!

20 minutes

Make Use-a-Ten
Flash Cards

Management individuals

Materials 10 triangle flash cards (Achieving Facts Fluency Support Master 4), 2 different-colored markers, previously made flash cards, practice record form and certificate (Achieving Facts Fluency Support Masters 11 and 15)

- Distribute triangle-shaped flash cards. Remind children to cut them out and put names or initials on the back. Have children make the flash cards shown below.

- When finished, children may find a partner and practice addition and subtraction facts with the use-a-ten flash cards.

- After practicing the use-a-ten facts only, children may add these cards to their previously made set of triangle cards and take them home for further practice. Practice minutes may be recorded and records returned to school to be exchanged for a certificate.

Basic Facts Workshop 12

Strategy Review

Introduce It!

15 minutes

Tens Again

Management whole class
Materials overhead projector, teacher-made transparencies of number wheel (Achieving Facts Fluency Support Master 8)

- Show a number wheel on the overhead projector. Write + 5 in the center. Write the numbers 2-9 in any order in the inner circle.

- Tell children the number wheel will help them practice adding. Ask children to identify each sum, then write it in the outer circle.

- Use a second transparency to make a subtraction wheel. Write − 6 in the center. Write the numbers

7-15 in any order in the inner circle.

- Ask children to identify each difference, then write it in the outer circle.

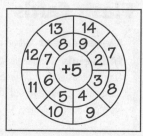 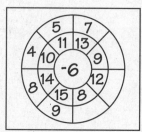

Tips

Remind children to use the count up, count back, doubles and near doubles strategies.

Develop It!

20 minutes

Make a Number Wheel

Management individuals or pairs
Materials number wheel (Achieving Facts Fluency Support Master 8)

- Distribute 2 number wheels to each child.

- To create an addition wheel, have children write + 6, + 7, + 8, or + 9 in the center. Then, ask them to fill in the inner circle with the numbers 9-17 in any order.

- Children should exchange both number wheels with a partner. Partners write appropriate answers in the outer circles of the wheels, then return the wheels to their partner who will check the answers for accuracy.

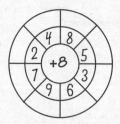 

Tips

Have children write the subtraction sentences if they become confused by the presentation of the numbers in the wheel.

15 minutes

Use Flash Cards to Practice

Management pairs
Materials previously made sets of triangle flash cards

- Remind children that they have already practiced all of the addition and subtraction facts. Now they will review to see which ones are now easy for them, and which ones they will want to practice more.

- Have children take out all previously made triangle flash cards.

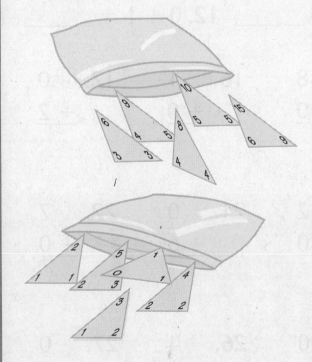

- Working with a partner, each child should go through all cards. If they know all facts for a card, they put it in one pile. If they have difficulty with any facts for a card, they put it in a second pile.

- Each partner should work on facts they have difficulty with for 5-10 minutes. Then have them go through just those cards again.

- Children may want to take their cards home for more practice.

Name_____ Date _____

1A ◢ BASIC FACTS

Adding and Subtracting Zero

Add.

1. $0 + 7 =$ __7__   2. $0 + 2 =$ _____   3. $3 + 0 =$ _____

4. $2 + 0 =$ _____   5. $1 + 0 =$ _____   6. $0 + 9 =$ _____

7. $4 + 0 =$ _____   8. $0 + 6 =$ _____   9. $0 + 8 =$ _____

10. $8 + 0 =$ _____   11. $5 + 0 =$ _____   12. $0 + 1 =$ _____

13.	14.	15.	16.	17.
0 +1	5 +0	8 +0	1 +0	0 +2

18.	19.	20.	21.	22.
6 +0	5 +0	2 +0	0 +6	7 +0

23.	24.	25.	26.	27.
0 +9	3 +0	0 +7	4 +0	0 +4

Name_____ Date _____

1B BASIC FACTS

Adding and Subtracting Zero

Subtract.

1.	2	2.	5	3.	8	4.	3	5.	4
	-0		-5		-0		-0		-0
	$\overline{2}$								

6.	1	7.	3	8.	6	9.	1	10.	4
	-0		-3		-0		-1		-0

11.	8	12.	5	13.	9	14.	7	15.	4
	-8		-5		-9		-0		-4

16.	6	17.	7	18.	5	19.	6	20.	0
	-6		-7		-0		-6		-0

21.	4	22.	8	23.	2	24.	9	25.	5
	-0		-0		-2		-0		-5

Name_____   Date _____

◢2A◣ BASIC FACTS

Counting On 1, 2, 3 to Add

Circle the greater addend. Count on to add.

1. ⑤ + 3 = __8__   2. 2 + 7 = _____   3. 1 + 8 = _____

4. 9 + 1 = _____   5. 3 + 4 = _____   6. 5 + 2 = _____

7. 1 + 6 = _____   8. 8 + 1 = _____   9. 7 + 3 = _____

Add.

10. 1   11. 1   12. 3   13. 9   14. 1
    + 9   + 2   + 8   + 2   + 3

15. 4   16. 9   17. 2   18. 8   19. 7
    + 2   + 3   + 3   + 2   + 1

20. 3   21. 6   22. 2   23. 4   24. 1
    + 7   + 3   + 6   + 1   + 3

◢ 2B ◣ BASIC FACTS

Counting On 1, 2, 3 to Add

Count on to add.

1. 4
    +2
    6

2. 2
    +9

3. 1
    +3

4. 5
    +3

5. 8
    +1

6. 2
    +2

7. 1
    +9

8. 6
    +3

9. 9
    +3

10. 4
    +3

11. 7
    +2

12. 8
    +2

13. 1
    +4

14. 1
    +8

15. 5
    +5

16. 1
    +5

17. 2
    +3

18. 3
    +4

19. 2
    +6

20. 7
    +3

21. 3
    +9

22. 9
    +2

23. 2
    +5

24. 8
    +3

25. 2
    +4

Name_____ Date _____

3A ◢ BASIC FACTS

Counting Back

Count back to subtract.

1. $8 - 1 = $ ___7___   2. $7 - 2 = $ _____   3. $6 - 1 = $ _____

4. $8 - 3 = $ _____   5. $5 - 1 = $ _____   6. $7 - 3 = $ _____

7. $9 - 2 = $ _____   8. $6 - 3 = $ _____   9. $4 - 1 = $ _____

10. $8 - 2 = $ _____   11. $3 - 1 = $ _____   12. $5 - 2 = $ _____

13. $\begin{array}{r} 9 \\ -3 \\ \hline \end{array}$ 14. $\begin{array}{r} 3 \\ -2 \\ \hline \end{array}$ 15. $\begin{array}{r} 2 \\ -1 \\ \hline \end{array}$ 16. $\begin{array}{r} 9 \\ -2 \\ \hline \end{array}$ 17. $\begin{array}{r} 4 \\ -1 \\ \hline \end{array}$

18. $\begin{array}{r} 4 \\ -3 \\ \hline \end{array}$ 19. $\begin{array}{r} 5 \\ -2 \\ \hline \end{array}$ 20. $\begin{array}{r} 7 \\ -1 \\ \hline \end{array}$ 21. $\begin{array}{r} 4 \\ -2 \\ \hline \end{array}$ 22. $\begin{array}{r} 3 \\ -3 \\ \hline \end{array}$

23. $\begin{array}{r} 9 \\ -1 \\ \hline \end{array}$ 24. $\begin{array}{r} 8 \\ -2 \\ \hline \end{array}$ 25. $\begin{array}{r} 6 \\ -3 \\ \hline \end{array}$ 26. $\begin{array}{r} 5 \\ -3 \\ \hline \end{array}$ 27. $\begin{array}{r} 6 \\ -2 \\ \hline \end{array}$

Name_____   Date _____

3B BASIC FACTS

Counting Back

Count back to subtract.

1. $9 - 3 =$ __6__   2. $9 - 2 =$ ____   3. $7 - 1 =$ ____

4. $8 - 2 =$ ____   5. $7 - 3 =$ ____   6. $6 - 3 =$ ____

7. $4 - 2 =$ ____   8. $4 - 1 =$ ____   9. $5 - 1 =$ ____

10. $9 - 1 =$ ____   11. $5 - 3 =$ ____   12. $3 - 2 =$ ____

13. $\begin{array}{r} 8 \\ -3 \\ \hline \end{array}$ 14. $\begin{array}{r} 6 \\ -1 \\ \hline \end{array}$ 15. $\begin{array}{r} 5 \\ -2 \\ \hline \end{array}$ 16. $\begin{array}{r} 7 \\ -2 \\ \hline \end{array}$ 17. $\begin{array}{r} 4 \\ -3 \\ \hline \end{array}$

18. $\begin{array}{r} 6 \\ -3 \\ \hline \end{array}$ 19. $\begin{array}{r} 7 \\ -3 \\ \hline \end{array}$ 20. $\begin{array}{r} 9 \\ -3 \\ \hline \end{array}$ 21. $\begin{array}{r} 5 \\ -3 \\ \hline \end{array}$ 22. $\begin{array}{r} 6 \\ -2 \\ \hline \end{array}$

23. $\begin{array}{r} 3 \\ -1 \\ \hline \end{array}$ 24. $\begin{array}{r} 9 \\ -2 \\ \hline \end{array}$ 25. $\begin{array}{r} 4 \\ -2 \\ \hline \end{array}$ 26. $\begin{array}{r} 8 \\ -1 \\ \hline \end{array}$ 27. $\begin{array}{r} 3 \\ -2 \\ \hline \end{array}$

4A ◢ BASIC FACTS

Counting Up

Count up to find the missing part.
Write the number sentence.

1.
Whole 9	
Part 6	Part 3

$$\underline{6} + \underline{3} = \underline{9}$$

2.
Whole 8	
Part 5	Part

_____ + _____ = _____

3.
Whole 7	
Part 4	Part

_____ + _____ = _____

4.
Whole 12	
Part 9	Part

_____ + _____ = _____

Name_____   Date _____

4B ◣ BASIC FACTS

Counting Up

Count up to subtract.

1. 12 − 9 **3**	**2.** 7 − 6	**3.** 11 − 9	**4.** 8 − 5	**5.** 4 − 2
6. 9 − 6	**7.** 3 − 2	**8.** 10 − 9	**9.** 7 − 4	**10.** 5 − 2
11. 10 − 7	**12.** 6 − 3	**13.** 5 − 4	**14.** 8 − 6	**15.** 6 − 4
16. 9 − 8	**17.** 9 − 7	**18.** 7 − 5	**19.** 9 − 6	**20.** 10 − 8
21. 6 − 5	**22.** 11 − 8	**23.** 5 − 3	**24.** 12 − 9	**25.** 6 − 4

Name_____ Date _____

5A ◢ BASIC FACTS

Strategy Review

Add or subtract.

1. 9   12
   +3   -9
   ──   ──
   12   3

2. 0   9
   +9   -0
   ──   ──

3. 9   11
   +2   -9
   ──   ──

4. 1   9
   +8   -8
   ──   ──

5. 4   5
   +1   -4
   ──   ──

6. 4   6
   +2   -4
   ──   ──

7. 8   11
   +3   -8
   ──   ──

8. 6   8
   +2   -7
   ──   ──

9. 2   10
   +8   -8
   ──   ──

10. 8   10
    +2   -8
    ──   ──

11. 7   8
    +1   -7
    ──   ──

12. 7   9
    +2   -8
    ──   ──

13. 1   10
    +9   -1
    ──   ──

14. 0   4
    +4   -0
    ──   ──

15. 7   10
    +3   -7
    ──   ──

Name_____ Date _____

5B ◤ BASIC FACTS

Strategy Review

Count on, back, or up.

1. $\begin{array}{r} 2 \\ -1 \\ \hline \end{array}$	**2.** $\begin{array}{r} 7 \\ +3 \\ \hline \end{array}$	**3.** $\begin{array}{r} 12 \\ -9 \\ \hline \end{array}$	**4.** $\begin{array}{r} 8 \\ -3 \\ \hline \end{array}$	**5.** $\begin{array}{r} 8 \\ +2 \\ \hline \end{array}$
6. $\begin{array}{r} 2 \\ +6 \\ \hline \end{array}$	**7.** $\begin{array}{r} 8 \\ +3 \\ \hline \end{array}$	**8.** $\begin{array}{r} 11 \\ -9 \\ \hline \end{array}$	**9.** $\begin{array}{r} 7 \\ -3 \\ \hline \end{array}$	**10.** $\begin{array}{r} 2 \\ +7 \\ \hline \end{array}$
11. $\begin{array}{r} 9 \\ -7 \\ \hline \end{array}$	**12.** $\begin{array}{r} 9 \\ -3 \\ \hline \end{array}$	**13.** $\begin{array}{r} 9 \\ -2 \\ \hline \end{array}$	**14.** $\begin{array}{r} 6 \\ +3 \\ \hline \end{array}$	**15.** $\begin{array}{r} 10 \\ -2 \\ \hline \end{array}$
16. $\begin{array}{r} 7 \\ -5 \\ \hline \end{array}$	**17.** $\begin{array}{r} 11 \\ -3 \\ \hline \end{array}$	**18.** $\begin{array}{r} 2 \\ +5 \\ \hline \end{array}$	**19.** $\begin{array}{r} 2 \\ +9 \\ \hline \end{array}$	**20.** $\begin{array}{r} 10 \\ -3 \\ \hline \end{array}$
21. $\begin{array}{r} 4 \\ +3 \\ \hline \end{array}$	**22.** $\begin{array}{r} 8 \\ -5 \\ \hline \end{array}$	**23.** $\begin{array}{r} 2 \\ +4 \\ \hline \end{array}$	**24.** $\begin{array}{r} 6 \\ -4 \\ \hline \end{array}$	**25.** $\begin{array}{r} 9 \\ -6 \\ \hline \end{array}$

Name_____ Date _____

6A ◢ BASIC FACTS

Using Doubles to Add

Write the sum of the double.
Use the double to write the next sum.

1. $7 + 7 =$ __14__   so $8 + 7 =$ __15__   so $9 + 7 =$ __16__

2. $4 + 4 =$ ____   so $5 + 4 =$ ____   so $6 + 4 =$ ____

3. $5 + 5 =$ ____   so $6 + 5 =$ ____   so $7 + 5 =$ ____

4. $6 + 6 =$ ____   so $7 + 6 =$ ____   so $8 + 6 =$ ____

Write the sum. Use a double when it helps.

5.   5   6.   6   7.   7   8.   8   9.   8
   $+5$ $+5$ $+5$ $+8$ $+9$

10.   7   11.   7   12.   8   13.   4   14.   5
   $+7$ $+8$ $+7$ $+4$ $+4$

Name_____ Date _____

6B BASIC FACTS

Using Doubles to Add

Use a double. Add.

1. $4 + 4 = \underline{8}$ so $4 + 5 = \underline{9}$ so $4 + 6 = \underline{10}$

2. $6 + 6 = \underline{}$ so $6 + 7 = \underline{}$ so $6 + 8 = \underline{}$

3. $\begin{array}{r} 4 \\ +4 \\ \hline \end{array}$ **4.** $\begin{array}{r} 4 \\ +5 \\ \hline \end{array}$ **5.** $\begin{array}{r} 6 \\ +4 \\ \hline \end{array}$ **6.** $\begin{array}{r} 7 \\ +8 \\ \hline \end{array}$ **7.** $\begin{array}{r} 8 \\ +7 \\ \hline \end{array}$

8. $\begin{array}{r} 8 \\ +8 \\ \hline \end{array}$ **9.** $\begin{array}{r} 4 \\ +6 \\ \hline \end{array}$ **10.** $\begin{array}{r} 5 \\ +5 \\ \hline \end{array}$ **11.** $\begin{array}{r} 5 \\ +6 \\ \hline \end{array}$ **12.** $\begin{array}{r} 5 \\ +7 \\ \hline \end{array}$

13. $\begin{array}{r} 6 \\ +4 \\ \hline \end{array}$ **14.** $\begin{array}{r} 6 \\ +5 \\ \hline \end{array}$ **15.** $\begin{array}{r} 6 \\ +6 \\ \hline \end{array}$ **16.** $\begin{array}{r} 6 \\ +7 \\ \hline \end{array}$ **17.** $\begin{array}{r} 6 \\ +8 \\ \hline \end{array}$

18. $\begin{array}{r} 7 \\ +5 \\ \hline \end{array}$ **19.** $\begin{array}{r} 7 \\ +6 \\ \hline \end{array}$ **20.** $\begin{array}{r} 7 \\ +7 \\ \hline \end{array}$ **21.** $\begin{array}{r} 7 \\ +9 \\ \hline \end{array}$ **22.** $\begin{array}{r} 8 \\ +9 \\ \hline \end{array}$

Name_____ Date_____

7A BASIC FACTS

Using Doubles to Subtract

Think of a double. Write the other part.
Write the number sentence.

1.
| Whole 10 | |
| Part 5 | Part 5 |

$$\underline{10} - \underline{5} = \underline{5}$$

2.
| Whole 12 | |
| Part 5 | Part |

$$\underline{\quad} - \underline{\quad} = \underline{\quad}$$

3.
| Whole 11 | |
| Part 5 | Part |

$$\underline{\quad} - \underline{\quad} = \underline{\quad}$$

4.
| Whole 14 | |
| Part 7 | Part |

$$\underline{\quad} - \underline{\quad} = \underline{\quad}$$

Name_____ Date _____

7B BASIC FACTS

....

Using Doubles to Subtract

Subtract.

1. $8 - 4 =$ __4__ so $9 - 4 =$ __5__ so $10 - 4 =$ __6__

2. $10 - 5 =$ _____ so $11 - 5 =$ _____ so $12 - 5 =$ _____

3. $12 - 6 =$ _____ so $13 - 6 =$ _____ so $14 - 6 =$ _____

4.	5.	6.	7.	8.
8	10	9	9	11
−4	− 5	− 5	− 4	− 5

9.	10.	11.	12.	13.
14	11	13	12	15
− 7	− 6	− 7	− 6	− 7

14.	15.	16.	17.	18.
14	15	10	18	17
− 6	− 8	− 4	− 9	− 8

Name_____ Date _____

▲8A BASIC FACTS

Strategy Review

Count up, on, or back.

1.	10 − 7 **3**	2.	8 + 2	3.	6 − 3	4.	11 − 4	5.	4 + 3
6.	9 + 1	7.	2 + 9	8.	8 + 3	9.	7 + 3	10.	9 + 2
11.	10 − 2	12.	10 − 3	13.	10 − 9	14.	9 − 6	15.	9 + 3
16.	4 + 2	17.	11 − 2	18.	10 − 1	19.	8 − 7	20.	9 − 7
21.	12 − 9	22.	6 + 2	23.	12 − 3	24.	6 + 1	25.	5 + 3

Name_____ Date _____

8B BASIC FACTS

Strategy Review

Think about doubles and near doubles.

1. $\begin{array}{r} 8 \\ -4 \\ \hline 4 \end{array}$

2. $\begin{array}{r} 10 \\ -5 \\ \hline \end{array}$

3. $\begin{array}{r} 8 \\ +9 \\ \hline \end{array}$

4. $\begin{array}{r} 12 \\ -7 \\ \hline \end{array}$

5. $\begin{array}{r} 7 \\ +5 \\ \hline \end{array}$

6. $\begin{array}{r} 16 \\ -8 \\ \hline \end{array}$

7. $\begin{array}{r} 14 \\ -6 \\ \hline \end{array}$

8. $\begin{array}{r} 9 \\ -5 \\ \hline \end{array}$

9. $\begin{array}{r} 13 \\ -7 \\ \hline \end{array}$

10. $\begin{array}{r} 16 \\ -9 \\ \hline \end{array}$

11. $\begin{array}{r} 15 \\ -8 \\ \hline \end{array}$

12. $\begin{array}{r} 7 \\ +8 \\ \hline \end{array}$

13. $\begin{array}{r} 15 \\ -7 \\ \hline \end{array}$

14. $\begin{array}{r} 11 \\ -6 \\ \hline \end{array}$

15. $\begin{array}{r} 17 \\ -9 \\ \hline \end{array}$

16. $\begin{array}{r} 8 \\ +6 \\ \hline \end{array}$

17. $\begin{array}{r} 7 \\ +9 \\ \hline \end{array}$

18. $\begin{array}{r} 4 \\ +5 \\ \hline \end{array}$

19. $\begin{array}{r} 13 \\ -6 \\ \hline \end{array}$

20. $\begin{array}{r} 10 \\ -4 \\ \hline \end{array}$

21. $\begin{array}{r} 9 \\ +7 \\ \hline \end{array}$

22. $\begin{array}{r} 5 \\ +6 \\ \hline \end{array}$

23. $\begin{array}{r} 7 \\ +7 \\ \hline \end{array}$

24. $\begin{array}{r} 18 \\ -9 \\ \hline \end{array}$

25. $\begin{array}{r} 8 \\ +7 \\ \hline \end{array}$

Name_____   Date _____

9A BASIC FACTS

Using Ten to Add

Make a 10. Complete the number sentence.

1. $8 + 4$

$10 + \underline{2} = \underline{12}$

2. $9 + 5$

$10 + \underline{\quad} = \underline{\quad}$

3. $9 + 7$

$10 + \underline{\quad} = \underline{\quad}$

4. $8 + 5$

$10 + \underline{\quad} = \underline{\quad}$

5. $9 + 6$

$10 + \underline{\quad} = \underline{\quad}$

6. $6 + 8$

$10 + \underline{\quad} = \underline{\quad}$

7. $9 + 4$

$10 + \underline{\quad} = \underline{\quad}$

8. $8 + 7$

$10 + \underline{\quad} = \underline{\quad}$

9. $9 + 7$

$10 + \underline{\quad} = \underline{\quad}$

10. $7 + 5$

$10 + \underline{\quad} = \underline{\quad}$

Name_____ Date _____

9B BASIC FACTS

Using Ten to Add

Make a 10. Complete the number sentence.

1. $8 + 7$

$10 + \underline{5} = \underline{15}$

2. $9 + 4$

$10 + \underline{\hspace{1cm}} = \underline{\hspace{1cm}}$

3. $8 + 8$

$10 + \underline{\hspace{1cm}} = \underline{\hspace{1cm}}$

4. $9 + 7$

$10 + \underline{\hspace{1cm}} = \underline{\hspace{1cm}}$

5. $9 + 5$

$10 + \underline{\hspace{1cm}} = \underline{\hspace{1cm}}$

6. $8 + 5$

$10 + \underline{\hspace{1cm}} = \underline{\hspace{1cm}}$

7. $9 + 6$

$10 + \underline{\hspace{1cm}} = \underline{\hspace{1cm}}$

8. $8 + 4$

$10 + \underline{\hspace{1cm}} = \underline{\hspace{1cm}}$

9. $5 + 7$

$10 + \underline{\hspace{1cm}} = \underline{\hspace{1cm}}$

10. $4 + 9$

$10 + \underline{\hspace{1cm}} = \underline{\hspace{1cm}}$

Name_____   Date _____

10A BASIC FACTS

Using Ten to Subtract

Make a 10. Subtract.

1. 13
    − 9
    4

2. 12
    − 9

3. 16
    − 9

4. 15
    − 7

5. 17
    − 9

6. 11
    − 7

7. 16
    − 7

8. 17
    − 9

9. 14
    − 9

10. 11
    − 9

11. 13
    − 8

12. 11
    − 7

13. 16
    − 9

14. 15
    − 8

15. 18
    − 9

16. 14
    − 8

17. 17
    − 9

18. 14
    − 9

19. 13
    − 9

20. 13
    − 8

21. 15
    − 9

22. 16
    − 9

23. 15
    − 9

24. 17
    − 8

25. 11
    − 9

Name_____   Date _____

◢ BASIC FACTS
10B

....

Using Ten to Subtract

Make a 10. Subtract.

1. 12 $- 7$ 5	**2.** 17 $- 9$	**3.** 15 $- 7$	**4.** 14 $- 7$	**5.** 16 $- 8$
6. 18 $- 9$	**7.** 12 $- 9$	**8.** 15 $- 8$	**9.** 17 $- 8$	**10.** 13 $- 9$
11. 16 $- 7$	**12.** 14 $- 8$	**13.** 11 $- 7$	**14.** 13 $- 8$	**15.** 16 $- 9$
16. 15 $- 7$	**17.** 12 $- 8$	**18.** 18 $- 9$	**19.** 13 $- 7$	**20.** 11 $- 8$
21. 17 $- 9$	**22.** 16 $- 7$	**23.** 14 $- 8$	**24.** 11 $- 9$	**25.** 13 $- 9$

Name_____ Date _____

11A BASIC FACTS

Using Ten to Subtract

Make a 10. Subtract.

1. 11
   − 4
   7

2. 14
   − 6

3. 12
   − 5

4. 13
   − 4

5. 12
   − 7

6. 12
   − 4

7. 15
   − 9

8. 14
   − 9

9. 12
   − 4

10. 13
    − 5

11. 12
    − 8

12. 13
    − 8

13. 15
    − 6

14. 13
    − 5

15. 11
    − 4

16. 14
    − 6

17. 13
    − 4

18. 12
    − 5

19. 11
    − 7

20. 16
    − 9

21. 14
    − 5

22. 12
    − 7

23. 13
    − 9

24. 16
    − 7

25. 15
    − 9

Name_____ Date _____

◢11B BASIC FACTS

Using Ten to Subtract

Write the answer.

1. 4 + 4 8	**2.** 11 − 7	**3.** 13 − 9	**4.** 5 + 8	**5.** 14 − 5
6. 12 − 7	**7.** 14 − 6	**8.** 12 − 8	**9.** 6 + 8	**10.** 16 − 9
11. 5 + 7	**12.** 9 + 6	**13.** 16 − 7	**14.** 8 + 4	**15.** 10 − 4
16. 15 − 9	**17.** 16 − 7	**18.** 9 + 7	**19.** 6 + 9	**20.** 14 − 8
21. 13 − 4	**22.** 7 + 9	**23.** 9 + 7	**24.** 5 + 9	**25.** 12 − 5

Name_____ Date _____

12A **BASIC FACTS**

Strategy Review

Add.

1. $\begin{array}{r} 1 \\ +7 \\ \hline 8 \end{array}$	**2.** $\begin{array}{r} 0 \\ +9 \\ \hline \end{array}$	**3.** $\begin{array}{r} 5 \\ +5 \\ \hline \end{array}$	**4.** $\begin{array}{r} 8 \\ +8 \\ \hline \end{array}$	**5.** $\begin{array}{r} 6 \\ +5 \\ \hline \end{array}$
6. $\begin{array}{r} 9 \\ +4 \\ \hline \end{array}$	**7.** $\begin{array}{r} 9 \\ +8 \\ \hline \end{array}$	**8.** $\begin{array}{r} 6 \\ +5 \\ \hline \end{array}$	**9.** $\begin{array}{r} 9 \\ +9 \\ \hline \end{array}$	**10.** $\begin{array}{r} 7 \\ +6 \\ \hline \end{array}$
11. $\begin{array}{r} 3 \\ +4 \\ \hline \end{array}$	**12.** $\begin{array}{r} 8 \\ +2 \\ \hline \end{array}$	**13.** $\begin{array}{r} 6 \\ +9 \\ \hline \end{array}$	**14.** $\begin{array}{r} 2 \\ +7 \\ \hline \end{array}$	**15.** $\begin{array}{r} 8 \\ +5 \\ \hline \end{array}$
16. $\begin{array}{r} 4 \\ +6 \\ \hline \end{array}$	**17.** $\begin{array}{r} 7 \\ +7 \\ \hline \end{array}$	**18.** $\begin{array}{r} 2 \\ +0 \\ \hline \end{array}$	**19.** $\begin{array}{r} 7 \\ +0 \\ \hline \end{array}$	**20.** $\begin{array}{r} 9 \\ +7 \\ \hline \end{array}$
21. $\begin{array}{r} 6 \\ +6 \\ \hline \end{array}$	**22.** $\begin{array}{r} 4 \\ +8 \\ \hline \end{array}$	**23.** $\begin{array}{r} 7 \\ +9 \\ \hline \end{array}$	**24.** $\begin{array}{r} 4 \\ +5 \\ \hline \end{array}$	**25.** $\begin{array}{r} 8 \\ +9 \\ \hline \end{array}$

Name_____   Date_____

12B BASIC FACTS
Strategy Review

Subtract.

1. 8 − 7	**2.** 12 − 5	**3.** 13 − 6	**4.** 11 − 7	**5.** 15 − 9
6. 10 − 8	**7.** 11 − 6	**8.** 14 − 8	**9.** 17 − 9	**10.** 16 − 8
11. 9 − 3	**12.** 13 − 7	**13.** 17 − 8	**14.** 15 − 9	**15.** 18 − 9
16. 12 − 7	**17.** 8 − 4	**18.** 11 − 5	**19.** 13 − 8	**20.** 10 − 7
21. 8 − 5	**22.** 13 − 4	**23.** 15 − 6	**24.** 10 − 4	**25.** 10 − 8

Basic Facts Workshop 1
Addition and Subtraction Facts

Copyright © Houghton Mifflin Company. All rights reserved.

Review

10 minutes

Counting On and Back to Add and Subtract

Management whole class

- Write 9 + 3 on the board.

- Ask students how the counting on strategy could help them find the answer. **When adding 1, 2, or 3 to a number, start at the larger number and count on from there.** Repeat with 2 + 9 and 8 + 3.

- Write 11 − 3 on the board.

- Ask students how they could figure out the answer to this basic subtraction fact. **Use the strategy of counting back. Start with the larger number and count back.** Repeat with 10 − 3 and 13 − 4.

- Write 8 − 9 on the board. Ask students if counting back would be a good way to figure out this fact. **No, because it's too hard to keep track of counting back 9 places.**

- Remind students that when subtracting, counting back works well if the number being subtracted is small, and counting on works well if the numbers being subtracted are close together.

- Students can practice these strategies by finding several similar basic facts for which counting on or back will help. For example, 9 − 2, 9 − 6, and 11 − 9.

Practice

30 minutes

Count On and Back with Flash Cards

Management individuals, then pairs
Materials for each student: 2 different-colored markers, 24 triangle flash cards (Achieving Facts Fluency Support Master 4), practice minutes record and certificate (Achieving Facts Fluency Support Masters 9 and 13)

- Have students make flash cards like the ones shown, with the top number written in one color and the bottom two numbers written in a second color, for the following fact families: 1,1,2; 1,2,3; 1,3,4; 1,4,5; 1,5,6; 1,6,7; 1,7,8; 1,8,9; 1,9,10; 2,2,4; 2,3,5; 2,4,6; 2,5,7; 2,6,8; 2,7,9; 2,8,10; 2,9,11; 3,3,6; 3,4,7; 3,5,8; 3,6,9; 3,7,10; 3,8,11; and 3,9,12.

- Students work with partners to review their addition and subtraction facts.

- One partner covers each corner in turn. If both numbers the partner sees are the same color, he or she states an addition fact. If the numbers are different colors, the partner states the subtraction fact.

- Encourage students to bring their flash cards home to practice, recording practice minutes. They may exchange completed records at school for a certificate.

Basic Facts Workshop 2

Doubles, Near Doubles Addition and Subtraction Facts

Review

25 minutes

Doubles and Near Doubles Facts

Management whole class
Materials overhead projector, blank transparencies, 18 counters

- Draw a vertical line down the center of a transparency. Place 7 counters on one side of the line. Have students count them. Ask, How many would there be if the counters were doubled? **14**

- Place 7 counters on the other half of the transparency. Ask students to name the addition fact shown. **7 + 7 = 14**

- Ask, If the whole is 14 and part is 7, which subtraction fact is known? **14 − 7 = 7**

- Repeat with other doubles facts such as 6 + 6, 8 + 8, and 9 + 9.

- Write 7 + 8 on a transparency. Show a row of 7 counters and a row of 8 counters.

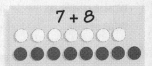

- Ask, How could a double help solve this fact?
  7 − 7 + 1 = 15 or
  8 + 8 − 1 = 15

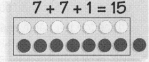

- Write 6 + 8 on a transparency. Place a row of 6 counters and a row of 8 counters on the projector. Ask students to use the double to find the sum.
  6 + 6 + 2 = 14 or 8 + 8 − 2 = 14

Practice

30 minutes

Make Doubles, Near Doubles Flash Cards

Management individuals, then pairs
Materials for each student: 2 different-colored markers, 5 triangle flash cards (Achieving Facts Fluency Support Master 4), 6 index cards, practice minutes record and certificate (Achieving Facts Fluency Support Masters 10 and 14)

- Remind students that doubles can help when adding two numbers. Tell them that when two numbers being added are close in value, near doubles can be used to find their sum.

- Give students an example of a near doubles fact, such as 5 + 4. Ask them to identify a double that might be helpful in finding the sum. **4 + 4**

- Ask, How many more need to be added to find the sum? **1** What is the sum? **4 + 4 + 1 = 9**

- Have students make flash cards for the following near doubles facts: 4,5,9; 6,7,13; 8,9,17; 7,8,15; and 5,6,11. Students should also make cards for these doubles facts: 4 + 4; 5 + 5; 6 + 6; 7 + 7; 8 + 8, and 9 + 9. Remind students to write their names or initials on the backs of their cards.

- Students may add these flash cards to their previously made set and take them home to practice. Remind them to record practice minutes. They may exchange completed records for a certificate.

Basic Facts Workshop 3

Using Ten to Add and Subtract

Review   20 minutes

Make a Ten Strategy

Management whole class

Materials overhead projector, 2 double ten-frame transparencies (Achieving Facts Fluency Support Master 3)

- Write 8 + 5 at the top of a transparency. Show 8 counters on the top ten-frame and 5 below.

- Ask, How could making a ten help you add these numbers? **Move 2 counters up to make 10 + 3 = 13** Write 8 + 5 = 13 at the top.

- Repeat with several examples, such as 9 + 6, 7 + 9, 8 + 6, 7 + 5, and 8 + 5.

- Write 15 − 6 at the top of a transparency. Show 15 counters on the ten-frames, 10 on top and 5 below.

- Ask how the making a ten strategy could help subtract 6 from 15. **Remove 5 counters from the bottom frame and 1 from the top frame.**

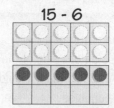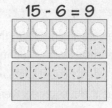

- Repeat with several examples, such as 13 − 6, 16 − 7, 15 − 8, 14 − 8, and 17 − 9.

Practice   30 minutes

Flash Cards for Make a Ten Facts

Management individuals, then pairs

Materials for each student: 2 different-colored markers, 10 triangle flash cards (Achieving Facts Fluency Support Master 4), practice minutes record and certificate (Achieving Facts Fluency Support Masters 10 and 14)

- Have students make flash cards like the ones shown. The top number should be written in one color, the bottom two numbers in another color. Students should make flash cards for the following facts: 4,6,10; 5,7,12; 6,8,14; 7,4,11; 8,4,12; 8,5,13; 9,4,13; 9,5,14; 9,6,15; and 9,7,16.

- When students have completed their make a ten flash cards, have them work with partners to review their addition and subtraction facts. Remind them to write their names or initials on the backs of their cards.

- Encourage students to bring their flash cards home to continue practicing their addition and subtraction facts. Remind them to keep a record of the minutes they practice. They may exchange completed records for a certificate.

Level 3

Basic Facts Workshop 4

Naming and Using Arrays in Multiplication

Review

15 minutes

Using Arrays to Multiply

Management whole class
Materials overhead projector, hundredths square transparencies (Achieving Facts Fluency Support Master 7), 35 counters

- Place 3 rows of 4 counters on a grid transparency. Outline the array. Ask students how many counters they see. **12** Then, ask students to name the array and the multiplication sentence it shows. **3 × 4, 3 × 4 = 12**

$3 \times 4 = 12$

- Remind students that the array shown can be named in two different ways, because when multiplying, the order of the factors does not change the product. Turn the grid transparency 90°. Ask students to name this array. **4 × 3**

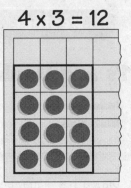

$4 \times 3 = 12$

- Repeat the activity, modeling arrays and writing two ways to name them for 2 × 6, 4 × 5, and 5 × 7.

Practice

30 minutes

Naming Arrays

Management pairs
Materials for each pair: a paper clip, a six-section spinner (Achieving Facts Fluency Support Master 6), 2-3 sheets of hundredths square paper (Achieving Facts Fluency Support Master 7)

- Distribute a spinner and 2-3 sheets of hundredths square paper to each pair. Have students label the spinner sections 1, 2, 3, 4, 5, and 6.

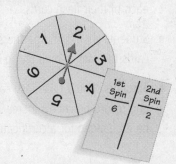

- One partner spins the spinner twice, while the other partner keeps a record of the numbers where the pointer lands.

- Using the two numbers that the pointer landed on, students should draw the array on their paper. Students may either draw circles to represent counters or outline the array. Partners work together to write two multiplication sentences for the array beside it. **Answers will vary. Possible answer:**
  2 × 6 = 12, 6 × 2 = 12

- Partners should switch roles and practice until each partner has had 10 turns.

Basic Facts Workshop 5
Multiplying by 1 and 2

25 minutes

1's and Doubles

Management whole class

Materials overhead projector, hundredths square transparencies (Achieving Facts Fluency Support Master 7)

- Draw a 1 × 4 array on a grid transparency. Ask students to name the array and the multiplication sentence it shows. **1 × 4; 1 × 4 = 4**

1 x 4

- Tell students you are going to double the array. Draw another 1 × 4 array below the first. Have students name the new array.
2 × 4 = 8

2 x 4

- Have students practice naming arrays. Draw a 2 × 6 array on a grid transparency and ask students to name it. **2 × 6**

- Repeat with several examples, such as 1 × 8 = 8 and 2 × 8 = 16; 1 × 3 = 3 and 2 × 3 = 6; and 1 × 9 = 9 and 2 × 9 = 18.

- Ask students to picture a 1 × 3 array and name it. **1 × 3** Then, ask them to double it and name the doubles multiplication fact. **2 × 3 = 6** Students may have trouble picturing arrays in their minds. If necessary, model arrays with connecting cubes or counters.

- Repeat, using facts such as 1 × 4 = 4 and 2 × 4 = 8; 1 × 2 = 2 and 2 × 2 = 4; and 1 × 7 = 7 and 2 × 7 = 14.

Practice

30 minutes

Make x1 and x2 Flash Cards

Management individuals, then pairs

Materials for each student: 32 index cards, practice minutes record and certificate (Achieving Facts Fluency Support Masters 9 and 13)

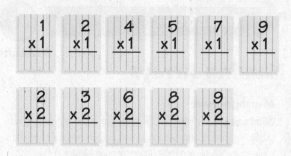

- Distribute index cards to each student and have them make flash cards like the ones below for the following facts: 1 × 1, 2 × 1, 3 × 1, 4 × 1, 5 × 1, 6 × 1, 7 × 1, 8 × 1, 9 × 1, 1 × 2, 1 × 3, 1 × 4, 1 × 5, 1 × 6, 1 × 7, 1 × 8, 1 × 9, 2 × 2, 3 × 2, 4 × 2, 5 × 2, 6 × 2, 7 × 2, 8 × 2, 9 × 2, 2 × 3, 2 × 4, 2 × 5, 2 × 6, 2 × 7, 2 × 8, and 2 × 9.

- Remind students to write their names on the backs of each of their flash cards.

- Students should find partners and use their flash cards to practice multiplying by 1 and 2.

- Students should take flash cards home to practice and record practice minutes. Completed records may be exchanged for a certificate.

Basic Facts Workshop 6
Multiplying by 4

Review

15 minutes

4's Are Double Doubles

Management whole class
Materials overhead projector, hundredths square transparencies (Achieving Facts Fluency Support Master 7)

- Draw a 2 × 4 array on a grid transparency. Have students name the multiplication sentence the array shows. **2 × 4 = 8**

- Ask students to recall how doubles helped them to figure out the 2's multiplication table. **Doubling the 1's multiplication table finds the 2's multiplication table.**

- Tell students that they can double the 2's

multiplication facts to figure out the 4's facts. Draw another 2 × 4 array below the first. Name the new array. **4 × 4** If necessary, point out that 4 × 4 = 16 is the double of 2 × 4 = 8.

- Repeat with several examples, such as 2 × 7 = 14 and 4 × 7 = 28; and 2 × 6 = 12 and 4 × 6 = 24.

- Ask students how to use the 2's multiplication table to figure out 4 × 3 = 12. **2 × 3 = 6, so 4 × 3 is double that, or 12.**

- Repeat with 4 × 5 = 20, 4 × 9 = 36, and 4 × 6 = 24.

- If necessary, model these multiplication sentences by drawing array diagrams.

Practice

30 minutes

Make x4 Flash Cards

Management individuals, then pairs
Materials for each student: 13 index cards, practice minutes record and certificate (Achieving Facts Fluency Support Masters 10 and 14)

- Distribute index cards to each student and have them make flash cards like those shown below for each of the following facts: 3 × 4, 4 × 3, 4 × 4, 4 × 5, 5 × 4, 4 × 6, 6 × 4, 4 × 7, 7 × 4, 8 × 4, 4 × 8, 4 × 9, and 9 × 4. Remind students to write their names or initials on the backs of their cards.

- Have students find partners and use their flash cards to practice multiplying by 4.

- Have students use their previously made flash cards to review the other multiplication facts for 4's that they already know.

- Students may want to take their flash cards home for additional practice. Remind students to keep a record of the minutes that they practice their multiplication facts, and return completed records to school in exchange for a certificate.

Basic Facts Workshop 7
Multiplying by 3

Review

🕐 25 minutes

Use 2's to Find 3's

Management whole class
Materials overhead projector, hundredths square transparency (Achieving Facts Fluency Support Master 7)

- Draw a 2 × 5 array on a grid transparency. Ask students to name the array and the multiplication sentence it shows. **2 × 5, 2 × 5 = 10**

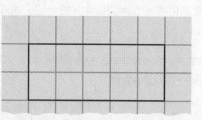

- Draw another row on the array to show 3 × 5. Ask students how knowing 2 × 5 = 10 can help them find 3 × 5. **Another 5 can be added to find the answer to 3 × 5.**

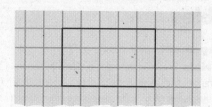

- Repeat the activity, using 2's facts to find 3 × 6, 3 × 4, 3 × 7, 3 × 8, and 3 × 9.

- Remind students that another way to find 3's is to skip-count. Have the class practice skip-counting by 3's to 30. Then ask students how skip-counting could help them figure out 3 × 3, 3 × 6, 3 × 8, and 3 × 9.

Practice

🕐 30 minutes

Make x3 Flash Cards

Management individuals, then pairs
Materials for each student: 11 index cards, practice minutes record and certificate (Achieving Facts Fluency Support Masters 10 and 14)

- Distribute index cards to each student and have them make flash cards like the ones shown below for the following facts: 3 × 3, 3 × 5, 3 × 6, 3 × 7, 3 × 8, 3 × 9, 5 × 3, 6 × 3, 7 × 3, 8 × 3, and 9 × 3.

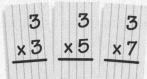

- When students are finished making their cards, they should find partners and use their flash cards to practice multiplying by 3. Remind students to first write their names or initials on the backs of their cards.

- Tell students to add in the flash cards they have already made for 3's facts (3 × 1, 1 × 3, 3 × 2, 2 × 3, 3 × 4, and 4 × 3).

- Encourage students to take all their flash cards home to continue practicing their multiplication facts. Remind students to record the number of minutes they practice at home, and return completed records to school to exchange for a certificate.

Basic Facts Workshop 8
Multiplying by 6

Review

20 minutes

Use 3's to Find 6's

Management whole class

Materials overhead projector, hundredths square transparency (Achieving Facts Fluency Support Master 7)

- Draw a 6 × 4 array on a grid transparency. Then draw a line to divide it into two 3 × 4 arrays.

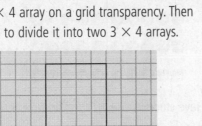

- Cover the bottom array with a piece of paper. Ask students how many squares are in the top 3 × 4 array. **12**

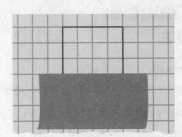

- Uncover the bottom array. Ask students how knowing 3 × 4 could help them find 6 × 4. **Double the 3 × 4 array to find 24.**

- Repeat the activity, modeling arrays for 6 × 7, 6 × 5, 6 × 8, 6 × 6, and 6 × 9, using 3's facts to determine 6's.

Practice

30 minutes

Make x6 Flash Cards

Management individuals, then pairs

Materials for each student: 8 index cards, practice minutes record and certificate (Achieving Facts Fluency Support Masters 10 and 14)

- Distribute index cards to students and have them make flash cards like those shown for the following facts: 6 × 5, 5 × 6, 6 × 7, 7 × 6, 6 × 8, 8 × 6, 6 × 9, and 9 × 6.

- Remind students to add the 6's flash cards they have already made (6 × 1, 1 × 6, 6 × 2, 2 × 6, 6 × 3, 3 × 6, 6 × 4, and 4 × 6) to the new set. Also remind them to write their names or initials on the backs of their cards. Then have students find partners. They can use their flash cards to practice their multiplication facts for 6.

- Invite students to take their flash cards home for additional practice. Remind them to keep a record of the minutes practiced. Students may exchange completed records at school for a certificate.

Achieving Facts Fluency 115

Basic Facts Workshop 9
Multiplying by 5

Review

20 minutes

Skip-Count or Use 10's

Management whole class

- Ask 5 students to stand in a line and hold up their hands as the class skip-counts by 5's to 50.

- Write 3×5 on the board. Ask students how to model this fact with hands or counters. **Holding up three hands or using three rows of five counters shows the fact.**

- Ask, If we know that $3 \times 5 = 15$, what other multiplication fact do we know? **$5 \times 3 = 15$**

- Repeat the activity, asking volunteers to direct students to show 5×5, 7×5, 4×5, 6×5, 9×5, and 8×5.

- Point out that another way to find 5's is to use 10's. Write $4 \times 10 = 40$ on the board. Ask students how knowing $4 \times 10 = 40$ could help them find 4×5. **4×5 is half of 4×10, or 20.**

$4 \times 10 = 40$

$4 \times 5 = 20$

- Have students use 10's to find 6×5, 3×5, 2×5, 8×5, 7×5, and 5×5.

- Ask students whether skip-counting or using a 10 is an easier way to find 5's. **Answers will vary.**

Practice

30 minutes

Make x5 Flash Cards

Management individuals, then pairs
Materials for each student: 7 index cards, practice minutes record and certificate (Achieving Facts Fluency Support Masters 10 and 14)

- Distribute index cards to each student and have them create flash cards like those shown for the following facts: 5×5, 5×7, 7×5, 5×8, 8×5, 5×9, and 9×5.

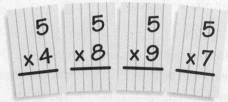

- Remind students to write their names or initials on the backs of their cards. Then, have them find partners and review and practice their multiplication facts for 5.

- Remind students that they already know ten of the facts for 5. Have them add their previously made flash cards (5×1, 1×5, 5×2, 2×5, 5×4, 4×5, 5×3, 3×5, 5×6, and 6×5) to the new ones.

- For additional practice, students may want to take their flash cards home. Remind them to keep a record of the minutes they practice. Students may return completed records to school in exchange for a certificate.

Basic Facts Workshop 10
Multiplying by 9

Review

25 minutes

Think Ten to Learn Nines

> **Management** whole class
> **Materials** overhead projector, hundredths square transparencies (Achieving Facts Fluency Support Master 7)

- Draw four 2 × 5 rectangles on a grid transparency to make ten frames. Ask students how many squares are in 4 tens. **40**

- Draw 9 dots in each ten-frame to model the multiplication fact 4 × 9. Ask the class how much less 4 × 9 is than 40. **It is 4 less** Then, ask students for the answer to 4 × 9. **4 less than 40, or 36**

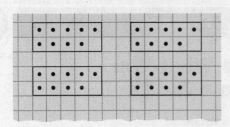

- Ask students why using the strategy of thinking about tens is a good way to help with 9's facts. **It's easy to multiply by 10 and then subtract.**

- Repeat the activity, modeling 3 × 9, 6 × 9, 5 × 9, and 2 × 9.

- Turn off the projector, and ask students to visualize ten-frames. Have them use tens to find the products for these multiplication facts: 7 × 9, 8 × 9, and 9 × 9.

Practice

30 minutes

Make x9 Flash Cards

> **Management** individuals, then pairs
> **Materials** for each student: 6 index cards, practice minutes record and certificate (Achieving Facts Fluency Support Masters 10 and 14)

- Distribute index cards and have students make flash cards like the ones shown for the following facts: 7 × 9, 9 × 7, 8 × 9, 9 × 8, 9 × 9, and 9 × 5.

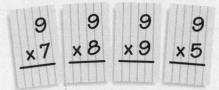

- When students complete their flash cards, have them add in the 9's cards they have already made. Then, have them practice multiplying by 9 with partners.

- Encourage students to take all of their flash cards home for additional practice. Remind them to keep a record of the number of minutes they work at home. Students may return completed records to school in exchange for a certificate.

Basic Facts Workshop 11
Multiplying by 7

Review

25 minutes

Use What You Know for 7's

Management whole class

Materials overhead projector, blank transparency, hundredths square transparencies (Achieving Facts Fluency Support Master 7)

- Remind the class that they have already practiced multiplying by 1's, 2's, 3's, 4's, 5's, 6's, and 9's. On a transparency write equations as shown. Have students determine the missing numbers. **2, 5, 1, 4, 3**

  ☐ × 7 = 14
  ☐ × 7 = 35
  ☐ × 7 = 7
  ☐ × 7 = 28
  ☐ × 7 = 21

- Ask students to identify which facts for 7 are missing from the list. **6 × 7 = 42, 7 × 7 = 49, 8 × 7 = 56, and 9 × 7 = 63**

- Draw a 7 × 7 array on a grid transparency. Tell students that if they cannot remember the product of 7 × 7, they could use the facts they do know to find the answer. Discuss different ways they might split the array into parts to find the product for 7 × 7. **7 × 5 plus 7 × 2; 7 × 1 plus 7 × 6; 7 × 3 plus 7 × 4**

  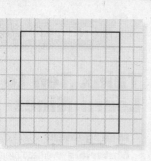

- Draw a 7 × 8 array on a grid transparency. In the event that students cannot remember the product, ask how they might split the array to use facts they do know to find 7 × 8. **7 × 4 plus 7 × 4; 7 × 2 plus 7 × 6; 7 × 3 plus 7 × 5**

Practice

30 minutes

Make x7 Flash Cards

Management individuals, then pairs

Materials for each student: 3 index cards, practice minutes record and certificate (Achieving Facts Fluency Support Masters 11 and 15)

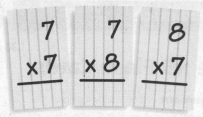

- Distribute index cards to each student.

- Have students make flash cards for the 3 remaining multiplication facts for 7: 7 × 7, 7 × 8, and 8 × 7. Remind them to write their names or initials on the backs of their cards.

- After they complete their flash cards, have students work with partners to practice multiplying by 7.

- For additional practice, students should take their flash cards home. Remind them to keep a record of the minutes that they practice. Students may return completed records to school in exchange for a certificate.

Basic Facts Workshop 12
Multiplying by 8

Review

25 minutes

Only One 8

Management whole class
Materials overhead projector, blank transparency, hundredths square transparency (Achieving Facts Fluency Support Master 7)

- Remind students that they have already practiced multiplying by 1's, 2's, 3's, 4's, 5's, 6's, 7's, and 9's. On a blank transparency, write equations as shown. Have students name the missing factors. **2, 7, 5, 4, 9, 3, 6**

☐ x 8 = 16
☐ x 8 = 56
☐ x 8 = 40
☐ x 8 = 32
☐ x 8 = 72
☐ x 8 = 24
☐ x 8 = 48

- Ask students to identify any facts for 8 other than 1 or 0 that are missing from the list. **The only fact left to learn is 8 × 8.**

- Draw an 8 × 8 array on a grid transparency. Tell students that if they cannot remember the answer to 8 × 8, they might use facts that they already know to figure out the product.

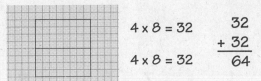

$$4 \times 8 = 32$$
$$4 \times 8 = 32$$

$$\begin{array}{r} 32 \\ + 32 \\ \hline 64 \end{array}$$

- Discuss different ways they might split the array into parts to find the product for 8 × 8. **Answers will vary. Possible answers: 4 × 8 plus 4 × 8; 1 × 8 plus 7 × 8; 2 × 8 plus 6 × 8; 3 × 8 plus 5 × 8.**

Practice

30 minutes

Make x8 Flash Cards

Management individuals, then pairs
Materials for each student: 1 index card, practice minutes record and certificate (Achieving Facts Fluency Support Masters 11 and 15)

- Distribute index cards to students. Have them make flash cards as shown for the following fact: 8 × 8.

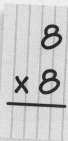

- Have students add this card to their previously made sets of 8's facts (8 × 1, 1 × 8, 8 × 2, 2 × 8, 8 × 3, 3 × 8, 8 × 4, 4 × 8, 8 × 5, 5 × 8, 8 × 6, 6 × 8, 8 × 7, 7 × 8, 8 × 9, and 9 × 8).

- Have students use their flash cards to practice 8's multiplication facts with a partner.

- For additional practice, students may want to take their flash cards home. Remind them to keep track of the number of minutes they practice. Students may return completed records to school in exchange for a certificate.

Name_____ Date _____

1A BASIC FACTS

Addition and Subtraction Facts

Add.

1.	2	2.	3	3.	8	4.	3	5.	7
	+ 4		+ 5		+ 1		+ 4		+ 2

6.	1	7.	2	8.	2	9.	7	10.	0
	+ 0		+ 6		+ 8		+ 1		+ 6

Add or subtract. Find a pattern. Write the next number sentence.

11. 1 + 6 = _____

    2 + 6 = _____

    3 + 6 = _____

    _____ + _____ = _____

13. 7 − 2 = _____

    8 − 2 = _____

    9 − 2 = _____

    _____ − _____ = _____

12. 3 + 3 = _____

    4 + 3 = _____

    5 + 3 = _____

    _____ + _____ = _____

14. 9 − 5 = _____

    9 − 6 = _____

    9 − 7 = _____

    _____ − _____ = _____

Name_____ Date _____

1B BASIC FACTS

Addition and Subtraction Facts

Find the greater number. Count on to add.

1. $6 + 1 =$ _____   2. $3 + 4 =$ _____   3. $5 + 2 =$ _____

4. $3 + 7 =$ _____   5. $6 + 2 =$ _____   6. $1 + 8 =$ _____

7. $2 + 9 =$ _____   8. $3 + 5 =$ _____   9. $4 + 2 =$ _____

Find the difference.

10. $\begin{array}{r}5\\-3\\\hline\end{array}$ 11. $\begin{array}{r}7\\-4\\\hline\end{array}$ 12. $\begin{array}{r}8\\-6\\\hline\end{array}$ 13. $\begin{array}{r}10\\-7\\\hline\end{array}$ 14. $\begin{array}{r}4\\-0\\\hline\end{array}$

15. $\begin{array}{r}6\\-5\\\hline\end{array}$ 16. $\begin{array}{r}4\\-2\\\hline\end{array}$ 17. $\begin{array}{r}9\\-6\\\hline\end{array}$ 18. $\begin{array}{r}6\\-4\\\hline\end{array}$ 19. $\begin{array}{r}7\\-6\\\hline\end{array}$

20. $\begin{array}{r}5\\-2\\\hline\end{array}$ 21. $\begin{array}{r}6\\-3\\\hline\end{array}$ 22. $\begin{array}{r}8\\-5\\\hline\end{array}$ 23. $\begin{array}{r}7\\-3\\\hline\end{array}$ 24. $\begin{array}{r}6\\-0\\\hline\end{array}$

25. $\begin{array}{r}9\\-3\\\hline\end{array}$ 26. $\begin{array}{r}8\\-2\\\hline\end{array}$ 27. $\begin{array}{r}9\\-5\\\hline\end{array}$ 28. $\begin{array}{r}4\\-3\\\hline\end{array}$ 29. $\begin{array}{r}7\\-5\\\hline\end{array}$

Name_____ Date _____

◢2A BASIC FACTS

Doubles, Near Doubles Addition and Subtraction Facts

Write a double that helps. Add.

1. 6
   + 5   +_____

2. 8
   + 9   +_____

3. 7
   + 6   +_____

4. 6
   + 5   +_____

5. 8
   + 9   +_____

6. 7
   + 6   +_____

Find the difference.

7. 5
   − 3

8. 7
   − 4

9. 8
   − 6

10. 10
    − 5

11. 4
    − 0

12. 16
    − 8

13. 4
    − 2

14. 12
    − 6

15. 8
    − 4

16. 7
    − 6

Look for doubles first. Then add.

17. 2 + 3 + 4 = _____

18. 3 + 3 + 5 = _____

19. 4 + 5 + 5 = _____

20. 2 + 7 + 3 = _____

Name_____ Date _____

2B BASIC FACTS

Doubles, Near Doubles Addition and Subtraction Facts

Add.

1. 4
  + 4

2. 7
  + 6

3. 2
  + 8

4. 6
  + 3

5. 4
  + 5

6. 9
  + 9

7. 5
  + 5

8. 3
  + 3

9. 5
  + 6

10. 8
  + 7

11. 8
  + 8

12. 1
  + 2

13. 6
  + 6

14. 7
  + 7

15. 3
  + 7

Draw a line to match. Subtract.

16. 16 − 8 = _____   A. 18
                            − 9

17. 9 − 5 = _____   B. 16
                            − 8

18. 18 − 9 = _____   C. 9
                            − 5

Name_____ Date _____

3A BASIC FACTS

··

Using Ten to Add and Subtract

Add. Make a ten to help.

1. 9 + 5 = _____   2. 4 + 7 = _____   3. 5 + 8 = _____

4. 6 + 8 = _____   5. 4 + 9 = _____   6. 7 + 9 = _____

7. 8 + 9 = _____   8. 4 + 8 = _____   9. 9 + 6 = _____

Subtract.

10. 10
    − 3

11. 6
    − 4

12. 7
    − 5

13. 9
    − 6

14. 8
    − 3

15. 6
    − 2

16. 10
    − 2

17. 11
    − 1

18. 10
    − 8

19. 11
    − 9

20. 8
    − 5

21. 7
    − 4

22. 7
    − 6

23. 8
    − 2

24. 9
    − 7

25. 11
    − 3

26. 10
    − 7

27. 8
    − 6

28. 10
    − 4

29. 8
    − 4

Name_____ Date _____

3B BASIC FACTS

Using Ten to Add and Subtract

Subtract. Make a ten to help.

1. $13 - 8 = $ _____   **2.** $15 - 9 = $ _____   **3.** $16 - 8 = $ _____

4. $12 - 9 = $ _____   **5.** $14 - 8 = $ _____   **6.** $17 - 8 = $ _____

Add or subtract.

7. $9 + 6 = $ _____   **8.** $16 - 8 = $ _____   **9.** $4 + 9 = $ _____

10. $18 - 9 = $ _____   **11.** $13 - 5 = $ _____   **12.** $7 + 7 = $ _____

13. $11 - 6 = $ _____   **14.** $14 - 8 = $ _____   **15.** $7 + 8 = $ _____

16. $12 - 7 = $ _____   **17.** $6 + 6 = $ _____   **18.** $10 - 6 = $ _____

19. $17 - 9 = $ _____   **20.** $9 + 7 = $ _____   **21.** $13 - 8 = $ _____

22. $15 - 8 = $ _____   **23.** $5 + 6 = $ _____   **24.** $7 + 9 = $ _____

Find the missing number.

25. $12 - $ _____ $= 3$ **26.** $14 - $ _____ $= 7$ **27.** $11 - $ _____ $= 9$

28. $16 - $ _____ $= 7$ **29.** $13 - $ _____ $= 5$ **30.** $12 - $ _____ $= 7$

Name_____   Date _____

4A ◢ BASIC FACTS

Naming and Using Arrays in Multiplication

Write one addition sentence and one multiplication sentence to describe each array.

1. • • • • •
   • • • • •
   • • • • •

   _____ = _____

   _____ = _____

2. • • • • • • •
   • • • • • • •

   _____ = _____

   _____ = _____

Solve.

3. $2 + 2 =$ _____

   $2 \times 2 =$ _____

4. $2 + 2 + 2 =$ _____

   $3 \times 2 =$ _____

5. $2 + 2 + 2 + 2 =$ _____

   $4 \times 2 =$ _____

6. $2 + 2 + 2 + 2 + 2 =$ _____

   $5 \times 2 =$ _____

7. $9 \times 2 =$ _____

8. $8 \times 2 =$ _____

Draw counters to show the array. Then write the product.

9. [grid]

   $2 \times 7 =$ _____

10. [grid]

   $6 \times 2 =$ _____

11. [grid]

   $4 \times 2 =$ _____

Name_____ Date _____

4B ▸ BASIC FACTS
··
Naming and Using Arrays in Multiplication

Draw counters to show the array. Then find the product.

1.

   $3 \times 6 = $ _____

2.

   $3 \times 8 = $ _____

3.

   $3 \times 5 = $ _____

Multiply. Think of doubles or the order property.

4. $2 \times 7 = $ _____   **5.** $6 \times 2 = $ _____   **6.** $2 \times 9 = $ _____

7. $4 \times 2 = $ _____   **8.** $2 \times 8 = $ _____   **9.** $2 \times 5 = $ _____

10. $2 \times 3 = $ _____   **11.** $9 \times 2 = $ _____   **12.** $2 \times 2 = $ _____

13. $5 \times 3 = $ _____   **14.** $4 \times 3 = $ _____   **15.** $3 \times 7 = $ _____

Use estimation. Write < or >.

16. $4 \times 3 = 12$, so 3×3 _____ 12   **17.** $7 \times 2 = 14$, so 7×3 _____ 14

18. $3 \times 2 = 6$, so 4×2 _____ 6   **19.** $8 \times 3 = 24$, so 9×3 _____ 24

20. $3 \times 3 = 9$, so 4×3 _____ 9   **21.** $6 \times 3 = 18$, so 7×3 _____ 18

Name_____   Date _____

5A ▸ BASIC FACTS

Multiplying by 1 and 2

Multiply.

1. $\begin{array}{r} 1 \\ \times\ 2 \\ \hline \end{array}$
2. $\begin{array}{r} 2 \\ \times\ 3 \\ \hline \end{array}$
3. $\begin{array}{r} 4 \\ \times\ 1 \\ \hline \end{array}$
4. $\begin{array}{r} 1 \\ \times\ 7 \\ \hline \end{array}$
5. $\begin{array}{r} 6 \\ \times\ 2 \\ \hline \end{array}$

6. $\begin{array}{r} 1 \\ \times\ 1 \\ \hline \end{array}$
7. $\begin{array}{r} 7 \\ \times\ 1 \\ \hline \end{array}$
8. $\begin{array}{r} 9 \\ \times\ 2 \\ \hline \end{array}$
9. $\begin{array}{r} 1 \\ \times\ 8 \\ \hline \end{array}$
10. $\begin{array}{r} 1 \\ \times\ 5 \\ \hline \end{array}$

11. $\begin{array}{r} 4 \\ \times\ 2 \\ \hline \end{array}$
12. $\begin{array}{r} 1 \\ \times\ 6 \\ \hline \end{array}$
13. $\begin{array}{r} 2 \\ \times\ 2 \\ \hline \end{array}$
14. $\begin{array}{r} 1 \\ \times\ 4 \\ \hline \end{array}$
15. $\begin{array}{r} 1 \\ \times\ 3 \\ \hline \end{array}$

16. $\begin{array}{r} 2 \\ \times\ 5 \\ \hline \end{array}$
17. $\begin{array}{r} 2 \\ \times\ 7 \\ \hline \end{array}$
18. $\begin{array}{r} 6 \\ \times\ 1 \\ \hline \end{array}$
19. $\begin{array}{r} 2 \\ \times\ 4 \\ \hline \end{array}$
20. $\begin{array}{r} 1 \\ \times\ 9 \\ \hline \end{array}$

Use mental math. Write just the answer.

21. $5 \times 1 \times 2 =$ _____
22. $7 \times 0 \times 2 =$ _____

23. $1 \times 2 \times 8 =$ _____
24. $3 \times 2 \times 1 =$ _____

25. $4 \times 2 \times 1 =$ _____
26. $2 \times 2 \times 1 =$ _____

Name_____ Date _____

5B BASIC FACTS

Multiplying by 1 and 2

Multiply. Think of doubles.

1. $2 \times 3 =$ _____   2. $2 \times 5 =$ _____   3. $2 \times 4 =$ _____

4. $2 \times 9 =$ _____   5. $2 \times 2 =$ _____   6. $2 \times 8 =$ _____

Multiply.

7. $1 \times 4 =$ _____   8. $1 \times 8 =$ _____   9. $6 \times 2 =$ _____

10. $9 \times 1 =$ _____   11. $1 \times 3 =$ _____   12. $2 \times 2 =$ _____

13. $1 \times 5 =$ _____   14. $7 \times 2 =$ _____   15. $2 \times 9 =$ _____

16.	17.	18.	19.	20.
1	7	5	1	2
$\times 2$	$\times 1$	$\times 2$	$\times 9$	$\times 1$

21.	22.	23.	24.	25.
1	1	8	1	2
$\times 1$	$\times 6$	$\times 2$	$\times 4$	$\times 6$

26.	27.	28.	29.	30.
8	1	3	2	4
$\times 1$	$\times 3$	$\times 2$	$\times 7$	$\times 2$

Name_____   Date _____

6A ▸ BASIC FACTS

Multiplying by 4

Write one addition sentence and one
multiplication sentence to describe each array.

1. • • • •
   • • • •

2. • • •
   • • •
   • • •
   • • •

_____ = _____

_____ = _____

_____ = _____

_____ = _____

Multiply.

3. $4 \times 3 =$ _____

4. $4 \times 8 =$ _____

5. $7 \times 4 =$ _____

6. $5 \times 4 =$ _____

7. $4 \times 2 =$ _____

8. $4 \times 4 =$ _____

9.   4
  $\times\,7$

10.   4
  $\times\,4$

11.   4
  $\times\,3$

12.   9
  $\times\,4$

13.   5
  $\times\,4$

14.   4
  $\times\,6$

15.   3
  $\times\,4$

16.   7
  $\times\,4$

17.   4
  $\times\,8$

18.   2
  $\times\,4$

6B
BASIC FACTS

Name_____ Date _____

Multiplying by 4

Multiply. Think of doubles or the order property.

1. $2 \times 7 =$ _____   2. $6 \times 2 =$ _____   3. $2 \times 9 =$ _____

4. $4 \times 2 =$ _____   5. $2 \times 8 =$ _____   6. $2 \times 5 =$ _____

7. $2 \times 3 =$ _____   8. $9 \times 2 =$ _____   9. $2 \times 2 =$ _____

Multiply.

10. $4 \times 3 =$ _____   11. $4 \times 8 =$ _____   12. $7 \times 4 =$ _____

13. $5 \times 4 =$ _____   14. $4 \times 2 =$ _____   15. $4 \times 4 =$ _____

16. $9 \times 4 =$ _____   17. $4 \times 6 =$ _____   18. $8 \times 4 =$ _____

19. $1 \times 4 =$ _____   20. $2 \times 4 =$ _____   21. $6 \times 4 =$ _____

22. $4 \times 7 =$ _____   23. $4 \times 1 =$ _____   24. $4 \times 9 =$ _____

25. $3 \times 4 =$ _____   26. $4 \times 5 =$ _____   27. $4 \times 6 =$ _____

28. $4 \times 8 =$ _____   29. $4 \times 2 =$ _____   30. $7 \times 4 =$ _____

Name_____ Date _____

7A ◢ BASIC FACTS

Multiplying by 3

Multiply.

1. 2
   × 3

2. 5
   × 3

3. 6
   × 3

4. 4
   × 3

5. 9
   × 3

6. 8
   × 3

7. 7
   × 3

8. 3
   × 3

9. 3
   × 9

10. 3
   × 5

11. 3
   × 6

12. 3
   × 2

Think of multiplication facts. Complete the tables.

	x	2
13.	6	12
14.	7	
15.	3	
16.	4	
17.	5	

	x	3
18.		27
19.	6	
20.		12
21.		24
22.		15

Name_____ Date _____

7B BASIC FACTS
Multiplying by 3

Match.

1. $3 \times 4 =$ _____   **a.** 9×1

2. $3 \times 5 =$ _____   **b.** 9×2

3. $3 \times 6 =$ _____   **c.** 6×2

4. $7 \times 3 =$ _____   **d.** 5×3

5. $3 \times 2 =$ _____   **e.** 1×3

6. $3 \times 3 =$ _____   **f.** 3×7

7. $3 \times 1 =$ _____   **g.** 6×1

Write pairs of factors for each product.

8. ____ $\times$ ____ $= 4$ 9. ____ $\times$ ____ $= 8$

10. ____ $\times$ ____ $= 3$ 11. ____ $\times$ ____ $= 5$

12. ____ $\times$ ____ $= 6$ 13. ____ $\times$ ____ $= 10$

14. ____ $\times$ ____ $= 7$ 15. ____ $\times$ ____ $= 9$

16. ____ $\times$ ____ $= 12$ 17. ____ $\times$ ____ $= 15$

Name_____ Date _____

8A BASIC FACTS

Multiplying by 6

Multiply.

1.	3 $\times\,6$	**2.** 5 $\times\,6$	**3.** 6 $\times\,2$	**4.** 4 $\times\,6$	**5.** 0 $\times\,6$

1.   3   **2.**   5   **3.**   6   **4.**   4   **5.**   0
     $\times\,6$ $\times\,6$ $\times\,2$ $\times\,6$ $\times\,6$

6.   1   **7.**   6   **8.**   9   **9.**   8   **10.**   6
     $\times\,6$ $\times\,4$ $\times\,6$ $\times\,6$ $\times\,2$

Compare. Write <, >, or =.

11. 5×6 _____ 3×6 **12.** 4×3 _____ 2×6

13. 3×3 _____ 6×2 **14.** 3×2 _____ 6×1

Multiply.

15. $6 \times 3 =$ _____   **16.** $6 \times 0 =$ _____   **17.** $9 \times 6 =$ _____

18. $5 \times 6 =$ _____   **19.** $6 \times 1 =$ _____   **20.** $7 \times 6 =$ _____

21. $2 \times 6 =$ _____   **22.** $6 \times 4 =$ _____   **23.** $6 \times 6 =$ _____

24. $6 \times 8 =$ _____   **25.** $3 \times 6 =$ _____   **26.** $6 \times 5 =$ _____

Name_____ Date _____

8B ▸ BASIC FACTS

Multiplying by 6

**Draw an array for each multiplication sentence.
Find the product.**

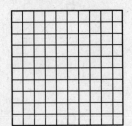   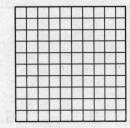

1. $6 \times 3 = $ _____   **2.** $2 \times 6 = $ _____

Multiply.

3. $\begin{array}{r} 6 \\ \times\,6 \\ \hline \end{array}$	**4.** $\begin{array}{r} 6 \\ \times\,4 \\ \hline \end{array}$	**5.** $\begin{array}{r} 9 \\ \times\,6 \\ \hline \end{array}$	**6.** $\begin{array}{r} 3 \\ \times\,6 \\ \hline \end{array}$	**7.** $\begin{array}{r} 6 \\ \times\,2 \\ \hline \end{array}$
8. $\begin{array}{r} 7 \\ \times\,6 \\ \hline \end{array}$	**9.** $\begin{array}{r} 8 \\ \times\,6 \\ \hline \end{array}$	**10.** $\begin{array}{r} 4 \\ \times\,6 \\ \hline \end{array}$	**11.** $\begin{array}{r} 0 \\ \times\,6 \\ \hline \end{array}$	**12.** $\begin{array}{r} 6 \\ \times\,8 \\ \hline \end{array}$
13. $\begin{array}{r} 2 \\ \times\,9 \\ \hline \end{array}$	**14.** $\begin{array}{r} 5 \\ \times\,6 \\ \hline \end{array}$	**15.** $\begin{array}{r} 8 \\ \times\,3 \\ \hline \end{array}$	**16.** $\begin{array}{r} 6 \\ \times\,1 \\ \hline \end{array}$	**17.** $\begin{array}{r} 3 \\ \times\,2 \\ \hline \end{array}$

Name_____   Date _____

9A ▶ BASIC FACTS

Multiplying by 5

Multiply.

1.	3	2.	5	3.	7	4.	2	5.	5
	× 5		× 6		× 5		× 5		× 8

6.	5	7.	9	8.	6	9.	8	10.	5
	× 4		× 5		× 5		× 5		× 9

Compare. Write < or >.

11. 5×6 _____ 3×6

12. 5×7 _____ 9×5

13. 5×8 _____ $5 + 8$

14. 5×9 _____ 4×8

Complete the multiplication table.

	x	6
15.	6	
16.	2	
17.	8	
18.	7	
19.	9	

Name_____ Date _____

9B ◢ BASIC FACTS
....
Multiplying by 5

Multiply.

1. $5 \times 2 =$ _____   **2.** $3 \times 5 =$ _____   **3.** $4 \times 5 =$ _____

   $2 \times 5 =$ _____ $5 \times 3 =$ _____ $5 \times 4 =$ _____

Find the products. Write whether each product is *greater than*, *less than*, or *equal to* 40.

4. $8 \times 5 =$ _____   _____

5. $5 \times 6 =$ _____   _____

6. $2 \times 5 =$ _____   _____

7. $9 \times 5 =$ _____   _____

8. $5 \times 10 =$ _____   _____

Multiply.

9. $8 \times 5 =$ _____   **10.** $5 \times 3 =$ _____   **11.** $8 \times 2 =$ _____

12. $9 \times 5 =$ _____   **13.** $4 \times 5 =$ _____   **14.** $6 \times 5 =$ _____

15. $0 \times 5 =$ _____   **16.** $7 \times 5 =$ _____   **17.** $5 \times 2 =$ _____

Name_____ Date _____

◣ 10A BASIC FACTS

Multiplying by 9

Complete the multiplication table. Use the table
to complete the number sentences.

x	9
1. 1	
2. 2	
3. 3	
4. 4	
5. 5	

6.   9
   × 2
   ☐

7.   4
   × 9
   ☐

8.   1
   × ☐
   9

9.   ☐
   × 9
   36

Multiply.

10. 9
  × 7

11. 9
  × 4

12. 9
  × 3

13. 9
  × 2

14. 4
  × 9

15. 8
  × 9

16. 5
  × 9

17. 9
  × 9

18. 3
  × 9

19. 2
  × 9

Name _____ Date _____

10B ◣ BASIC FACTS

Multiplying by 9

Complete the chart below, using what you know about nines facts.

1.	1×9	=	
2.	2×9	=	
3.	3×9	=	
4.	4×9	=	
5.	5×9	=	
6.	6×9	=	
7.	7×9	=	
8.	8×9	=	
9.	9×9	=	

Multiply.

10. $\begin{array}{r} 9 \\ \times\,4 \\ \hline \end{array}$
11. $\begin{array}{r} 9 \\ \times\,6 \\ \hline \end{array}$
12. $\begin{array}{r} 4 \\ \times\,5 \\ \hline \end{array}$
13. $\begin{array}{r} 7 \\ \times\,6 \\ \hline \end{array}$
14. $\begin{array}{r} 7 \\ \times\,9 \\ \hline \end{array}$

15. $9 \times 5 =$ _____

16. $9 \times 1 =$ _____

17. $0 \times 9 =$ ___

Fill in the blanks.

18. $2 \times$ ____ $= 18$

19. $3 \times 9 =$ ____

20. $9 \times$ ____ $= 9$

21. ____ $\times 9 = 36$

22. ____ $\times 9 = 9$

23. $9 \times$ ____ $= 45$

Name_____   Date _____

11A ⏵ BASIC FACTS

Multiplying by 7

**Find the products. Write whether each product is
greater than, *less than*, or *equal to* 30.**

1. $7 \times 3 =$ _____

2. $7 \times 8 =$ _____

3. $6 \times 7 =$ _____

4. $5 \times 7 =$ _____

Multiply.

5.	6.	7.	8.	9.
3 $\times\,7$	4 $\times\,7$	7 $\times\,6$	5 $\times\,7$	7 $\times\,5$

10.	11.	12.	13.	14.
8 $\times\,7$	2 $\times\,7$	1 $\times\,7$	0 $\times\,7$	9 $\times\,7$

Use estimation. Write < or >.

15. $7 \times 3 = 21$, so 7×4 ____ 21

16. $7 \times 2 = 14$, so 7×1 ____ 14

17. $7 \times 5 = 35$, so 7×4 ____ 35

18. $7 \times 6 = 42$, so 7×7 ____ 42

Name_____ Date _____

11B ◣ BASIC FACTS

Multiplying by 7

Multiply.

x	7
1. 8	
2. 3	
3. 9	
4. 6	
5. 7	

6. $7 \times 7 =$ _____   **7.** $6 \times 8 =$ _____   **8.** $1 \times 7 =$ _____

9. $8 \times 7 =$ _____   **10.** $7 \times 4 =$ _____   **11.** $7 \times 3 =$ _____

12. $4 \times 7 =$ _____   **13.** $6 \times 7 =$ _____   **14.** $7 \times 9 =$ _____

15. $7 \times 8 =$ _____   **16.** $3 \times 9 =$ _____   **17.** $2 \times 7 =$ _____

Multiply and add using mental math. Work from left to right. Write just the answer.

18. $7 \times 8 + 3 =$ _____   **19.** $7 \times 4 + 2 =$ _____

20. $2 \times 7 + 4 =$ _____   **21.** $3 \times 7 + 3 =$ _____

Name_____   Date _____

12A ▸ BASIC FACTS

Multiplying by 8

Multiply.

1. $\begin{array}{r} 8 \\ \times\ 6 \\ \hline \end{array}$	**2.** $\begin{array}{r} 8 \\ \times\ 7 \\ \hline \end{array}$	**3.** $\begin{array}{r} 8 \\ \times\ 3 \\ \hline \end{array}$	**4.** $\begin{array}{r} 6 \\ \times\ 8 \\ \hline \end{array}$	**5.** $\begin{array}{r} 5 \\ \times\ 8 \\ \hline \end{array}$
6. $\begin{array}{r} 7 \\ \times\ 8 \\ \hline \end{array}$	**7.** $\begin{array}{r} 8 \\ \times\ 4 \\ \hline \end{array}$	**8.** $\begin{array}{r} 0 \\ \times\ 8 \\ \hline \end{array}$	**9.** $\begin{array}{r} 8 \\ \times\ 8 \\ \hline \end{array}$	**10.** $\begin{array}{r} 1 \\ \times\ 8 \\ \hline \end{array}$

Complete the table.

	x	8
11.	2	
12.		64
13.	7	
14.	4	
15.		40

Multiply and add using mental math. Work from left to right. Write just the answer.

16. $5 \times 8 + 2 =$ _____

17. $1 \times 8 + 4 =$ _____

18. $8 \times 2 + 2 =$ _____

19. $3 \times 8 + 1 =$ _____

Name_____ Date _____

◤12B BASIC FACTS

Multiplying by 8

Multiply.

1. $8 \times 7 =$ _____ **2.** $8 \times 5 =$ _____ **3.** $8 \times 3 =$ _____

4. $1 \times 8 =$ _____ **5.** $4 \times 8 =$ _____ **6.** $8 \times 2 =$ _____

7. $8 \times 4 =$ _____ **8.** $8 \times 1 =$ _____ **9.** $6 \times 8 =$ _____

Complete the table with the facts you have learned. One column has been completed for you.

x	2	3	4	5	6	7	8	9
10. 2			8					
11. 3			12					
12. 4			16					
13. 5			20					
14. 6			24					
15. 7			28					
16. 8			32					
17. 9			36					

Compare. Write <, >, or =.

18. 2×8 ___ 3×5 **19.** 3×8 ___ 4×8 **20.** 8×4 ___ 5×9

21. 4×6 ___ 3×8 **22.** 2×8 ___ 3×5 **23.** 1×8 ___ $1 + 8$

Name_____   Date _____

BASIC FACTS: ADDITION

Find the sum. Use strategies to help you.

1. 4 +5	**2.** 2 +4	**3.** 0 +7	**4.** 6 +1	**5.** 8 +2	**6.** 1 +4
7. 5 +4	**8.** 8 +9	**9.** 6 +5	**10.** 9 +2	**11.** 7 +8	**12.** 5 +3
13. 9 +9	**14.** 1 +0	**15.** 3 +5	**16.** 6 +4	**17.** 5 +9	**18.** 6 +7
19. 1 +9	**20.** 8 +4	**21.** 1 +5	**22.** 3 +3	**23.** 8 +8	**24.** 6 +2
25. 5 +7	**26.** 3 +7	**27.** 3 +9	**28.** 5 +8	**29.** 7 +5	**30.** 2 +8

I need more practice with these facts:

Name_____ Date _____

BASIC FACTS: ADDITION

Find the sum. Use strategies to help you.

1. 0
    + 4

2. 9
    + 6

3. 7
    + 3

4. 4
    + 5

5. 1
    + 8

6. 3
    + 6

7. 5
    + 0

8. 2
    + 1

9. 9
    + 8

10. 7
     + 6

11. 7
     + 4

12. 4
     + 9

13. 4
     + 1

14. 8
     + 5

15. 5
     + 6

16. 4
     + 7

17. 1
     + 3

18. 7
     + 9

19. 3
     + 4

20. 2
     + 2

21. 8
     + 7

22. 9
     + 3

23. 9
     + 2

24. 7
     + 0

25. 1
     + 1

26. 6
     + 8

27. 5
     + 2

28. 0
     + 6

29. 3
     + 2

30. 0
     + 0

I need more practice with these facts:

Name_____ Date _____

BASIC FACTS: ADDITION

Find the sum. Use strategies to help you.

1. 4
  + 3

2. 6
  + 1

3. 8
  + 9

4. 2
  + 5

5. 2
  + 0

6. 2
  + 7

7. 0
  + 3

8. 7
  + 2

9. 5
  + 5

10. 9
  + 4

11. 8
  + 0

12. 3
  + 1

13. 6
  + 6

14. 2
  + 3

15. 8
  + 3

16. 4
  + 2

17. 6
  + 9

18. 0
  + 5

19. 4
  + 8

20. 4
  + 6

21. 2
  + 9

22. 0
  + 1

23. 9
  + 1

24. 1
  + 2

25. 5
  + 1

26. 9
  + 5

27. 7
  + 7

28. 4
  + 0

29. 9
  + 7

30. 8
  + 1

I need more practice with these facts:

Name_____ Date _____

BASIC FACTS: SUBTRACTION

Find the difference. Use strategies to help you.

1. 9 − 3	**2.** 16 − 8	**3.** 3 − 1	**4.** 7 − 6	**5.** 12 − 5	**6.** 14 − 9
7. 8 − 5	**8.** 4 − 0	**9.** 10 − 7	**10.** 11 − 2	**11.** 6 − 3	**12.** 1 − 1
13. 7 − 1	**14.** 8 − 8	**15.** 9 − 4	**16.** 5 − 5	**17.** 16 − 7	**18.** 10 − 6
19. 11 − 2	**20.** 9 − 2	**21.** 14 − 5	**22.** 13 − 6	**23.** 7 − 2	**24.** 1 − 0
25. 9 − 8	**26.** 5 − 4	**27.** 18 − 9	**28.** 12 − 8	**29.** 6 − 2	**30.** 15 − 8

I need more practice with these facts:

Name_____ Date _____

BASIC FACTS: SUBTRACTION

Find the difference. Use strategies to help you.

1. 5 −1	**2.** 3 −3	**3.** 9 −0	**4.** 15 −7	**5.** 11 −3	**6.** 8 −2
7. 9 −7	**8.** 3 −2	**9.** 14 −8	**10.** 2 −1	**11.** 6 −4	**12.** 7 −7
13. 10 −5	**14.** 13 −5	**15.** 8 −0	**16.** 13 −4	**17.** 8 −4	**18.** 17 −8
19. 2 −0	**20.** 11 −4	**21.** 16 −9	**22.** 10 −2	**23.** 7 −3	**24.** 2 −1
25. 9 −9	**26.** 5 −3	**27.** 12 −7	**28.** 7 −5	**29.** 12 −6	**30.** 15 −6

I need more practice with these facts:

Name_____   Date _____

BASIC FACTS: SUBTRACTION

Find the difference. Use strategies to help you.

1. 7 − 0	**2.** 4 − 3	**3.** 13 − 8	**4.** 17 − 9	**5.** 4 − 4	**6.** 11 − 7
7. 8 − 3	**8.** 14 − 6	**9.** 10 − 1	**10.** 0 − 0	**11.** 13 − 7	**12.** 9 − 5
13. 6 − 1	**14.** 11 − 5	**15.** 4 − 1	**16.** 10 − 9	**17.** 12 − 4	**18.** 3 − 0
19. 7 − 4	**20.** 12 − 9	**21.** 6 − 5	**22.** 8 − 1	**23.** 14 − 7	**24.** 10 − 4
25. 5 − 0	**26.** 12 − 3	**27.** 8 − 6	**28.** 4 − 2	**29.** 15 − 9	**30.** 8 − 7

I need more practice with these facts:

Name_____   Date _____

BASIC FACTS: MULTIPLICATION

Find the product. Use strategies to help you.

1. 2 × 5	2. 4 × 1	3. 8 × 7	4. 2 × 0	5. 4 × 3	6. 6 × 3
7. 6 × 9	8. 6 × 6	9. 0 × 6	10. 2 × 7	11. 6 × 8	12. 6 × 5
13. 5 × 7	14. 3 × 5	15. 4 × 7	16. 2 × 9	17. 2 × 8	18. 3 × 3
19. 6 × 2	20. 0 × 4	21. 7 × 9	22. 7 × 5	23. 3 × 4	24. 7 × 6
25. 3 × 7	26. 4 × 6	27. 8 × 5	28. 4 × 8	29. 9 × 1	30. 9 × 5

I need more practice with these facts:

Name_____ Date _____

BASIC FACTS: MULTIPLICATION

Find the product. Use strategies to help you.

1. 0 × 8	**2.** 9 × 7	**3.** 5 × 5	**4.** 3 × 6	**5.** 2 × 1	**6.** 8 × 3
7. 4 × 3	**8.** 7 × 0	**9.** 1 × 7	**10.** 6 × 1	**11.** 8 × 8	**12.** 5 × 9
13. 9 × 2	**14.** 9 × 3	**15.** 1 × 9	**16.** 2 × 3	**17.** 0 × 0	**18.** 4 × 1
19. 7 × 7	**20.** 5 × 4	**21.** 5 × 1	**22.** 7 × 3	**23.** 9 × 6	**24.** 3 × 0
25. 3 × 6	**26.** 3 × 1	**27.** 6 × 7	**28.** 9 × 8	**29.** 2 × 6	**30.** 9 × 4

I need more practice with these facts:

Name_____ Date _____

BASIC FACTS: MULTIPLICATION

Find the product. Use strategies to help you.

1. 1 × 1	**2.** 7 × 8	**3.** 4 × 5	**4.** 9 × 2	**5.** 0 × 7	**6.** 2 × 4
7. 8 × 9	**8.** 8 × 1	**9.** 1 × 6	**10.** 5 × 2	**11.** 7 × 4	**12.** 9 × 0
13. 5 × 6	**14.** 7 × 3	**15.** 8 × 6	**16.** 3 × 4	**17.** 5 × 8	**18.** 8 × 4
19. 9 × 9	**20.** 0 × 1	**21.** 4 × 4	**22.** 0 × 5	**23.** 3 × 8	**24.** 6 × 2
25. 2 × 2	**26.** 5 × 3	**27.** 8 × 0	**28.** 3 × 9	**29.** 9 × 6	**30.** 4 × 9

I need more practice with these facts:

Name_____ Date _____

BASIC FACTS: DIVISION

Find the quotient. Use strategies to help you.

1. $1\overline{)6}$ 2. $7\overline{)28}$ 3. $4\overline{)12}$ 4. $5\overline{)45}$ 5. $3\overline{)0}$ 6. $6\overline{)36}$

7. $3\overline{)27}$ 8. $2\overline{)10}$ 9. $8\overline{)8}$ 10. $9\overline{)63}$ 11. $3\overline{)21}$ 12. $6\overline{)12}$

13. $5\overline{)25}$ 14. $7\overline{)56}$ 15. $2\overline{)2}$ 16. $4\overline{)36}$ 17. $5\overline{)15}$ 18. $1\overline{)3}$

19. $5\overline{)35}$ 20. $3\overline{)9}$ 21. $1\overline{)9}$ 22. $2\overline{)4}$ 23. $6\overline{)0}$ 24. $8\overline{)48}$

25. $9\overline{)27}$ 26. $4\overline{)24}$ 27. $2\overline{)14}$ 28. $6\overline{)24}$ 29. $4\overline{)20}$ 30. $2\overline{)18}$

I need more practice with these facts:

Name_____   Date _____

BASIC FACTS: DIVISION

Find the quotient. Use strategies to help you.

1. 6)42   **2.** 4)32   **3.** 5)0   **4.** 1)2   **5.** 3)15   **6.** 8)64

7. 3)3   **8.** 6)18   **9.** 7)49   **10.** 3)6   **11.** 1)5   **12.** 8)40

13. 9)72   **14.** 5)30   **15.** 9)0   **16.** 4)16   **17.** 5)10   **18.** 7)21

19. 3)18   **20.** 6)6   **21.** 6)54   **22.** 2)16   **23.** 9)45   **24.** 7)14

25. 5)20   **26.** 1)0   **27.** 6)48   **28.** 4)28   **29.** 5)5   **30.** 7)35

I need more practice with these facts:

Name_____ Date _____

BASIC FACTS: DIVISION

Find the quotient. Use strategies to help you.

1. 1)4   **2.** 7)42   **3.** 8)24   **4.** 7)7   **5.** 2)12   **6.** 8)32

7. 6)30   **8.** 4)8   **9.** 2)0   **10.** 5)40   **11.** 7)0   **12.** 3)24

13. 1)7   **14.** 8)72   **15.** 2)16   **16.** 9)9   **17.** 9)54   **18.** 2)6

19. 7)63   **20.** 4)0   **21.** 9)81   **22.** 1)1   **23.** 9)36   **24.** 8)0

25. 5)45   **26.** 3)12   **27.** 9)18   **28.** 2)8   **29.** 8)56   **30.** 4)4

I need more practice with these facts:

Answers

Level 1

Worksheet 1A: **2.** 4 **3.** 8 **4.** 10 **5.** 6 **6.** 7 **7.** 3 **8.** 5

Worksheet 1B: Drawings will vary. **2.** 6 dots **3.** 7 dots **4.** 9 dots **5.** 4 dots **6.** 5 dots **7.** 2 dots **8.** 3 dots

Worksheet 2A: **2.** 7 **3.** 9 **4.** 5 **5.** 10 **6.** 4 **7.** 6 **8.** 8

Worksheet 2B: **2.** 4 **3.** 7 **4.** 8 **5.** 5 **6.** 9 **7.** 6 **8.** 3

Worksheet 3A: Drawings will vary. Possible answers include: $5 + 2$; $1 + 6$; $7 + 0$.

Worksheet 3B: **2.** $2 + 2 = 4$ **3.** $3 + 2 = 5$ **4.** $3 + 0 = 3$

Worksheet 4A: **2.** 9; $5 + 4 = 9$ **3.** 9; $7 + 2 = 9$ **4.** 9; $6 + 3 = 9$

Worksheet 4B: **2.** $6 + 4 = 10$ **3.** $10 + 0 = 10$ **4.** $7 + 3 = 10$

Worksheet 5A: Drawings will vary. **2.** 7 dots; 7 **3.** 9 dots; 9 **4.** 6 dots; 6 **5.** 4 dots; 4 **6.** 8 dots; 8

Worksheet 5B: **2.** 5 **3.** 0 **4.** 1 **5.** 0 **6.** 9 **7.** 0 **8.** 7 **9.** 4 **10.** 7 **11.** 0 **12.** 0 **13.** 3 **14.** 0 **15.** 8 **16.** 0 **17.** 0 **18.** 0 **19.** 9 **20.** 1 **21.** 2

Worksheet 6A: **2.** 17 **3.** 11 **4.** 13

Worksheet 6B: **2.** $10 + 2 = 12$ **3.** $10 + 6 = 16$ **4.** $10 + 8 = 18$

Worksheet 7A: **2.** $5 + 3 = 8$ **3.** $2 + 4 = 6$ **4.** $4 + 2 = 6$ **5.** $6 + 3 = 9$ **6.** $3 + 6 = 9$

Worksheet 7B: **2.** 5,5 **3.** 6,6 **4.** 5,5 **5.** 9,9 **6.** 6,6 **7.** 7,7 **8.** 10,10 **9.** 8,8 **10.** 8,8 **11.** 7,7 **12.** 9,9

Worksheet 8A: **2.** 8 **3.** 7 **4.** 2 **5.** 8 **6.** 9 **7.** 11 **8.** 6 **9.** 5 **10.** 4 **11.** 9 **12.** 10 **13.** 4 **14.** 7 **15.** 6 **16.** 10 **17.** 7 **18.** 8 **19.** 3 **20.** 9

Worksheet 8B: **2.** 8 **3.** 11 **4.** 9 **5.** 7 **6.** 10 **7.** 8 **8.** 9 **9.** 11 **10.** 4 **11.** 10 **12.** 9 **13.** 12 **14.** 9 **15.** 7 **16.** 6 **17.** 8 **18.** 8 **19.** 10 **20.** 5 **21.** 6

Worksheet 9A: **2.** 3 **3.** 7 **4.** 4 **5.** 7 **6.** 2 **7.** 9 **8.** 4 **9.** 2 **10.** 5 **11.** 6 **12.** 3 **13.** 1 **14.** 9 **15.** 1 **16.** 5 **17.** 2 **18.** 6 **19.** 7 **20.** 1

Worksheet 9B: **2.** 6 **3.** 4 **4.** 3 **5.** 4 **6.** 7 **7.** 8 **8.** 5 **9.** 5 **10.** 3 **11.** 7 **12.** 4 **13.** 6 **14.** 2 **15.** 2 **16.** 1 **17.** 5 **18.** 6 **19.** 4 **20.** 3 **21.** 5 **22.** 2 **23.** 2

Worksheet 10A: **2.** 1 **3.** 1 **4.** 1 **5.** 3 **6.** 2 **7.** 1 **8.** 2 **9.** 2 **10.** 2 **11.** 3 **12.** 1 **13.** 1 **14.** 3 **15.** 2 **16.** 2 **17.** 1 **18.** 2 **19.** 1 **20.** 3

Worksheet 10B: **2.** 5 **3.** 1 **4.** 3 **5.** 4 **6.** 1 **7.** 5 **8.** 3 **9.** 7 **10.** 3 **11.** 2 **12.** 1 **13.** 2 **14.** 1 **15.** 2 **16.** 3 **17.** 1 **18.** 2 **19.** 2 **20.** 3 **21.** 4

Worksheet 11A: **2.** 6 dots; $6 + 6 = 12$ **3.** 5 dots; $5 + 5 = 10$ **4.** 8 dots; $8 + 8 = 16$ **5.** 14 **6.** 18 **7.** 16 **8.** 12

Worksheet 11B: **2.** 10, 11, 11 **3.** 12, 13, 13 **4.** 14, 15, 15 **5.** 16, 17, 17

Worksheet 12A: **2.** 5 **3.** 4 **4.** 6 **5.** 6 **6.** 5 **7.** 6 **8.** 7 **9.** 8 **10.** 7 **11.** 9 **12.** 9 **13.** 6 **14.** 9 **15.** 8 **16.** 5 **17.** 8 **18.** 6 **19.** 8 **20.** 7 **21.** 7 **22.** 4

Worksheet 12B: **2.** 5 **3.** 6 **4.** 6 **5.** 7 **6.** 8 **7.** 8 **8.** 6 **9.** 9 **10.** 5 **11.** 4 **12.** 7 **13.** 6 **14.** 6 **15.** 3 **16.** 7 **17.** 9 **18.** 5 **19.** 8 **20.** 4 **21.** 9

Level 2

Worksheet 1A: **2.** 2 **3.** 3 **4.** 2 **5.** 1 **6.** 9 **7.** 4 **8.** 6 **9.** 8 **10.** 8 **11.** 5 **12.** 1 **13.** 1 **14.** 5 **15.** 8 **16.** 1 **17.** 2 **18.** 6 **19.** 5 **20.** 2 **21.** 6 **22.** 7 **23.** 9 **24.** 3 **25.** 7 **26.** 4 **27.** 4

Worksheet 1B: **2.** 0 **3.** 8 **4.** 3 **5.** 4 **6.** 1 **7.** 0 **8.** 6 **9.** 0 **10.** 4 **11.** 0 **12.** 0 **13.** 0 **14.** 7 **15.** 0 **16.** 0 **17.** 0 **18.** 5 **19.** 0 **20.** 0 **21.** 4 **22.** 8 **23.** 0 **24.** 9 **25.** 0

Worksheet 2A: **2.** 9 **3.** 9 **4.** 10 **5.** 7 **6.** 7 **7.** 7 **8.** 9 **9.** 10 **10.** 10 **11.** 3 **12.** 11 **13.** 11 **14.** 4 **15.** 6 **16.** 12 **17.** 5 **18.** 10 **19.** 8 **20.** 10 **21.** 9 **22.** 8 **23.** 5 **24.** 4

Worksheet 2B: **2.** 11 **3.** 4 **4.** 8 **5.** 9 **6.** 4 **7.** 10 **8.** 9 **9.** 12 **10.** 7 **11.** 9 **12.** 10 **13.** 5 **14.** 9 **15.** 10 **16.** 6 **17.** 5 **18.** 7 **19.** 8 **20.** 10 **21.** 12 **22.** 11 **23.** 7 **24.** 11 **25.** 6

Worksheet 3A: **2.** 5 **3.** 5 **4.** 5 **5.** 4 **6.** 4 **7.** 7 **8.** 3 **9.** 3 **10.** 6 **11.** 2 **12.** 3 **13.** 6 **14.** 1 **15.** 1 **16.** 7 **17.** 3 **18.** 1 **19.** 3 **20.** 6 **21.** 2 **22.** 0 **23.** 8 **24.** 6 **25.** 3 **26.** 2 **27.** 4

Worksheet 3B: **2.** 7 **3.** 6 **4.** 6 **5.** 4 **6.** 3 **7.** 2 **8.** 3 **9.** 4 **10.** 8 **11.** 2 **12.** 1 **13.** 5 **14.** 5 **15.** 3 **16.** 5 **17.** 1 **18.** 3 **19.** 4 **20.** 6 **21.** 2 **22.** 4 **23.** 2 **24.** 7 **25.** 2 **26.** 7 **27.** 1

Worksheet 4A: **2.** 3; $5 + 3 = 8$ **3.** 3; $4 + 3 = 7$ **4.** 3; $9 + 3 = 12$

Worksheet 4B: **2.** 1 **3.** 2 **4.** 3 **5.** 2 **6.** 3 **7.** 1 **8.** 1 **9.** 3 **10.** 3 **11.** 3 **12.** 3 **13.** 1 **14.** 2 **15.** 2 **16.** 1 **17.** 2 **18.** 2 **19.** 3 **20.** 2 **21.** 1 **22.** 3 **23.** 2 **24.** 3 **25.** 2

Worksheet 5A: **2.** 9; 9 **3.** 11; 2 **4.** 9; 1 **5.** 5; 1 **6.** 6; 2 **7.** 11; 3 **8.** 8; 1 **9.** 10; 2 **10.** 10; 2 **11.** 8; 1 **12.** 9; 1 **13.** 10; 9 **14.** 4; 4 **15.** 10; 3

Worksheet 5B: **2.** 10 **3.** 3 **4.** 5 **5.** 10 **6.** 8 **7.** 11 **8.** 2 **9.** 4 **10.** 9 **11.** 2 **12.** 6 **13.** 7 **14.** 9 **15.** 8 **16.** 2 **17.** 8 **18.** 7 **19.** 11 **20.** 7 **21.** 7 **22.** 3 **23.** 6 **24.** 2 **25.** 3

Worksheet 6A: **2.** 8, 9, 10 **3.** 10, 11, 12 **4.** 12, 13, 14 **5.** 10 **6.** 11 **7.** 12 **8.** 16 **9.** 17 **10.** 14 **11.** 15 **12.** 15 **13.** 8 **14.** 9

Worksheet 6B: **2.** 12, 13, 14 **3.** 8 **4.** 9 **5.** 10 **6.** 15 **7.** 15 **8.** 16 **9.** 10 **10.** 10 **11.** 11 **12.** 12 **13.** 10 **14.** 11 **15.** 12 **16.** 13 **17.** 14 **18.** 12 **19.** 13 **20.** 14 **21.** 16 **22.** 17

Worksheet 7A: **2.** 7; $12 - 5 = 7$ **3.** 6; $11 - 5 = 6$ **4.** 7; $14 - 7 = 7$

Worksheet 7B: **2.** 5, 6, 7 **3.** 6, 7, 8 **4.** 4 **5.** 6 **6.** 4 **7.** 5 **8.** 6 **9.** 7 **10.** 5 **11.** 6 **12.** 6 **13.** 8 **14.** 8 **15.** 7 **16.** 6 **17.** 9 **18.** 9

Worksheet 8A: **2.** 10 **3.** 4 **4.** 7 **5.** 7 **6.** 10 **7.** 11 **8.** 11 **9.** 10 **10.** 11 **11.** 8 **12.** 7 **13.** 1 **14.** 3 **15.** 12 **16.** 6 **17.** 9 **18.** 9 **19.** 1 **20.** 2 **21.** 3 **22.** 8 **23.** 9 **24.** 7 **25.** 8

Worksheet 8B: **2.** 5 **3.** 17 **4.** 5 **5.** 12 **6.** 8 **7.** 8 **8.** 4 **9.** 6 **10.** 7 **11.** 7 **12.** 15 **13.** 8 **14.** 5 **15.** 8 **16.** 14 **17.** 16 **18.** 9 **19.** 7 **20.** 6 **21.** 16 **22.** 11 **23.** 14 **24.** 9 **25.** 15

Worksheet 9A: 2. 4,14 3. 6,16 4. 3,13 5. 5,15 6. 4,14 7. 3,13 8. 5,15 9. 6,16 10. 2,12

Worksheet 9B: 2. 3,13 3. 6,16 4. 6,16 5. 4,14 6. 3,13 7. 5,15 8. 2,12 9. 2,12 10. 3,13

Worksheet 10A: 2. 3 3. 7 4. 8 5. 8 6. 4 7. 9 8. 8 9. 5 10. 2 11. 5 12. 4 13. 7 14. 7 15. 9 16. 6 17. 8 18. 5 19. 4 20. 5 21. 6 22. 7 23. 6 24. 9 25. 2

Worksheet 10B: 2. 8 3. 8 4. 7 5. 8 6. 9 7. 3 8. 7 9. 9 10. 4 11. 9 12. 6 13. 4 14. 5 15. 7 16. 8 17. 4 18. 9 19. 6 20. 3 21. 8 22. 9 23. 6 24. 2 25. 4

Worksheet 11A: 2. 8 3. 7 4. 9 5. 5 6. 8 7. 6 8. 5 9. 8 10. 8 11. 4 12. 5 13. 9 14. 8 15. 7 16. 8 17. 9 18. 7 19. 4 20. 7 21. 9 22. 5 23. 4 24. 9 25. 6

Worksheet 11B: 2. 4 3. 4 4. 13 5. 9 6. 5 7. 8 8. 4 9. 14 10. 7 11. 12 12. 15 13. 9 14. 12 15. 6 16. 6 17. 9 18. 16 19. 15 20. 6 21. 9 22. 16 23. 16 24. 14 25. 7

Worksheet 12A: 2. 9 3. 10 4. 16 5. 11 6. 13 7. 17 8. 11 9. 18 10. 13 11. 7 12. 10 13. 15 14. 9 15. 13 16. 10 17. 14 18. 2 19. 7 20. 16 21. 12 22. 12 23. 16 24. 9 25. 17

Worksheet 12B: 2. 7 3. 7 4. 4 5. 6 6. 2 7. 5 8. 6 9. 8 10. 8 11. 6 12. 6 13. 9 14. 6 15. 9 16. 5 17. 4 18. 6 19. 5 20. 3 21. 3 22. 9 23. 9 24. 6 25. 2

Level 3

Worksheet 1A: 1. 6 2. 8 3. 9 4. 7 5. 9 6. 1 7. 8 8. 10 9. 8 10. 6 11. 7, 8, 9, $4 + 6 = 10$ 12. 6, 7, 8, $6 + 3 = 9$ 13. 5, 6, 7, $10 - 2 = 8$ 14. 4, 3, 2, $9 - 8 = 1$

Worksheet 1B: 1. 7 2. 7 3. 7 4. 10 5. 8 6. 9 7. 11 8. 8 9. 6 10. 2 11. 3 12. 2 13. 3 14. 4 15. 1 16. 2 17. 3 18. 2 19. 1 20. 3 21. 3 22. 3 23. 4 24. 6 25. 6 26. 6 27. 4 28. 1 29. 2

Worksheet 2A: Answers will vary for doubles. 1. 11 2. 17 3. 13 4. 11 5. 17 6. 13 7. 2 8. 3 9. 2 10. 5 11. 4 12. 8 13. 2 14. 6 15. 4 16. 1 17. 9 18. 11 19. 14 20. 12

Worksheet 2B: 1. 8 2. 13 3. 10 4. 9 5. 9 6. 18 7. 10 8. 6 9. 11 10. 15 11. 16 12. 3 13. 12 14. 14 15. 10 16. B; 8 17. C; 4 18. A; 9

Worksheet 3A: 1. 14 2. 11 3. 13 4. 14 5. 13 6. 16 7. 17 8. 12 9. 15 10. 7 11. 2 12. 2 13. 3 14. 5 15. 4 16. 8 17. 10 18. 2 19. 2 20. 3 21. 3 22. 1 23. 6 24. 2 25. 8 26. 3 27. 2 28. 6 29. 4

Worksheet 3B: 1. 5 2. 6 3. 8 4. 3 5. 6 6. 9 7. 15 8. 8 9. 13 10. 9 11. 8 12. 14 13. 5 14. 6 15. 15 16. 5 17. 12 18. 4 19. 8 20. 16 21. 5 22. 7 23. 11 24. 16 25. 9 26. 7 27. 2 28. 9 29. 8 30. 5

Worksheet 4A: Answers will vary. Possible answers are given. 1. $10 + 5 = 15$, $5 \times 3 = 15$ 2. $7 + 7 = 14$, $7 \times 2 = 14$ 3. 4, 4 4. 6, 6 5. 8, 8 6. 10, 10 7. 18 8. 16 Drawings will vary. 9. 14 10. 12 11. 8

Worksheet 4B: Drawings will vary. 1. 18 2. 24 3. 15 4. 14 5. 12 6. 18 7. 8 8. 16 9. 10 10. 6 11. 18 12. 4 13. 15 14. 12 15. 21 16. < 17. > 18. > 19. > 20. > 21. >

Worksheet 5A: 1. 2 2. 6 3. 4 4. 7 5. 12 6. 1 7. 7 8. 18 9. 8 10. 5 11. 8 12. 6 13. 4 14. 4 15. 3 16. 10 17. 14 18. 6 19. 8 20. 9 21. 10 22. 0 23. 16 24. 6 25. 8 26. 4

Worksheet 5B: 1. 6 2. 10 3. 8 4. 18 5. 4 6. 16 7. 4 8. 8 9. 12 10. 9 11. 3 12. 4 13. 5 14. 14 15. 18 16. 2 17. 7 18. 10 19. 9 20. 2 21. 1 22. 6 23. 16 24. 4 25. 12 26. 8 27. 3 28. 6 29. 14 30. 8

Worksheet 6A: Answers will vary. Possible answers are given. 1. $4 + 4 = 8$, $4 \times 2 = 8$ 2. $4 + 4 + 4 = 12$, $4 \times 3 = 12$ 3. 12 4. 32 5. 28 6. 20 7. 8 8. 16 9. 28 10. 16 11. 12 12. 36 13. 20 14. 24 15. 12 16. 28 17. 32 18. 8

Worksheet 6B: 1. 14 2. 12 3. 18 4. 8 5. 16 6. 10 7. 6 8. 18 9. 4 10. 12 11. 32 12. 28 13. 20 14. 8 15. 16 16. 36 17. 24 18. 32 19. 4 20. 8 21. 24 22. 28 23. 4 24. 36 25. 12 26. 20 27. 24 28. 32 29. 8 30. 28

Worksheet 7A: 1. 6 2. 15 3. 18 4. 12 5. 27 6. 24 7. 21 8. 9 9. 27 10. 15 11. 18 12. 6 13. Answer given. 14. 14 15. 6 16. 8 17. 10 18. 9 19. 18 20. 4 21. 8 22. 5

Worksheet 7B: 1. c. 2. d. 3. b. 4. f. 5. g. 6. a. 7. e. Answers will vary. Possible answers are given. 8. 2×2 9. 4×2 10. 3×1 11. 1×5 12. 2×3 13. 5×2 14. 1×7 15. 3×3 16. 6×2 17. 5×3

Worksheet 8A: 1. 18 2. 30 3. 12 4. 24 5. 0 6. 6 7. 24 8. 54 9. 48 10. 12 11. > 12. = 13. < 14. = 15. 18 16. 0 17. 54 18. 30 19. 6 20. 42 21. 12 22. 24 23. 36 24. 48 25. 18 26. 30

Worksheet 8B: Drawings will vary. 1. 18 2. 12 3. 36 4. 24 5. 54 6. 18 7. 12 8. 42 9. 48 10. 24 11. 0 12. 48 13. 18 14. 30 15. 24 16. 6 17. 6

Worksheet 9A: 1. 15 2. 30 3. 35 4. 10 5. 40 6. 20 7. 45 8. 30 9. 40 10. 45 11. > 12. < 13. > 14. > 15. 36 16. 12 17. 48 18. 42 19. 54

Worksheet 9B: 1. 10, 10 2. 15, 15 3. 20, 20 4. 40, equal to 5. 30, less than 6. 10, less than 7. 45, greater than 8. 50, greater than 9. 40 10. 15 11. 16 12. 45 13. 20 14. 30 15. 0 16. 35 17. 10

Worksheet 10A: 1. 9 2. 18 3. 27 4. 36 5. 45 6. 18 7. 36 8. 9 9. 4 10. 63 11. 36 12. 27 13. 18 14. 36 15. 72 16. 45 17. 81 18. 27 19. 18

Worksheet 10B: 1. 9 2. 18 3. 27 4. 36 5. 45 6. 54 7. 63 8. 72 9. 81 10. 36 11. 54 12. 20 13. 42 14. 63 15. 45 16. 9 17. 0 18. 9 19. 27 20. 1 21. 4 22. 1 23. 5

Worksheet 11A: 1. 21, less than 2. 56, greater than 3. 42, greater than 4. 35, greater than 5. 21 6. 28 7. 42 8. 35 9. 35 10. 56 11. 14 12. 7 13. 0 14. 63 15. > 16. < 17. < 18. >

Worksheet 11B: 1. 56 2. 21 3. 63 4. 42 5. 49 6. 49 7. 48 8. 7 9. 56 10. 28 11. 21 12. 28 13. 42 14. 63 15. 56 16. 27 17. 14 18. 59 19. 30 20. 18 21. 24

Worksheet 12A: 1. 48 2. 56 3. 24 4. 48 5. 40 6. 56 7. 32 8. 0 9. 64 10. 8 11. 16 12. 8 13. 56 14. 32 15. 5 16.

42 **17.** 12 **18.** 18 **19.** 25

Worksheet 12B: **1.** 56 **2.** 40 **3.** 24 **4.** 8 **5.** 32 **6.** 16 **7.** 32 **8.** 8 **9.** 48 **10.** 4, 6, 10, 12, 14, 16, 18 **11.** 6, 9, 15, 18, 21, 24, 27 **12.** 8, 12, 20, 24, 28, 32, 36 **13.** 10, 15, 25, 30, 35, 40, 45 **14.** 12, 18, 30, 36, 42, 48, 54 **15.** 14, 21, 35, 42, 49, 56, 63 **16.** 16, 24, 40, 48, 56, 64, 72 **17.** 18, 27, 45, 54, 63, 72, 81 **18.** > **19.** < **20.** < **21.** = **22.** > **23.** <

Cumulative Practice

Practice 1 : **1.** 9 **2.** 6 **3.** 7 **4.** 7 **5.** 10 **6.** 5 **7.** 9 **8.** 17 **9.** 11 **10.** 11 **11.** 15 **12.** 8 **13.** 18 **14.** 1 **15.** 8 **16.** 10 **17.** 14 **18.** 13 **19.** 10 **20.** 12 **21.** 6 **22.** 6 **23.** 16 **24.** 8 **25.** 12 **26.** 10 **27.** 12 **28.** 13 **29.** 12 **30.** 10

Practice 2: **1.** 4 **2.** 15 **3.** 10 **4.** 9 **5.** 9 **6.** 9 **7.** 5 **8.** 3 **9.** 17 **10.** 13 **11.** 11 **12.** 13 **13.** 5 **14.** 13 **15.** 11 **16.** 11 **17.** 4 **18.** 16 **19.** 7 **20.** 4 **21.** 15 **22.** 12 **23.** 11 **24.** 7 **25.** 2 **26.** 14 **27.** 7 **28.** 6 **29.** 5 **30.** 0

Practice 3: **1.** 7 **2.** 7 **3.** 17 **4.** 7 **5.** 2 **6.** 9 **7.** 3 **8.** 9 **9.** 10 **10.** 13 **11.** 8 **12.** 4 **13.** 12 **14.** 5 **15.** 11 **16.** 6 **17.** 15 **18.** 5 **19.** 12 **20.** 10 **21.** 11 **22.** 1 **23.** 10 **24.** 3 **25.** 6 **26.** 14 **27.** 14 **28.** 4 **29.** 16 **30.** 9

Practice 4: **1.** 6 **2.** 8 **3.** 2 **4.** 1 **5.** 7 **6.** 5 **7.** 3 **8.** 4 **9.** 3 **10.** 9 **11.** 3 **12.** 0 **13.** 6 **14.** 0 **15.** 5 **16.** 0 **17.** 9 **18.** 4 **19.** 9 **20.** 7 **21.** 9 **22.** 7 **23.** 5 **24.** 1 **25.** 1 **26.** 1 **27.** 9 **28.** 4 **29.** 4 **30.** 7

Practice 5: **1.** 4 **2.** 0 **3.** 9 **4.** 8 **5.** 8 **6.** 6 **7.** 2 **8.** 1 **9.** 6 **10.** 1 **11.** 2 **12.** 0 **13.** 5 **14.** 8 **15.** 8 **16.** 9 **17.** 4 **18.** 9 **19.** 2 **20.** 7 **21.** 7 **22.** 8 **23.** 4 **24.** 1 **25.** 0 **26.** 2 **27.** 5 **28.** 2 **29.** 6 **30.** 9

Practice 6: **1.** 7 **2.** 1 **3.** 5 **4.** 8 **5.** 0 **6.** 4 **7.** 5 **8.** 8 **9.** 9 **10.** 0 **11.** 6 **12.** 4 **13.** 5 **14.** 6 **15.** 3 **16.** 1 **17.** 8 **18.** 3 **19.** 3 **20.** 3 **21.** 1 **22.** 7 **23.** 7 **24.** 6 **25.** 5 **26.** 9 **27.** 2 **28.** 2 **29.** 6 **30.** 1

Practice 7: **1.** 10 **2.** 4 **3.** 56 **4.** 0 **5.** 12 **6.** 18 **7.** 54 **8.** 36 **9.** 0 **10.** 14 **11.** 48 **12.** 30 **13.** 35 **14.** 15 **15.** 28 **16.** 18 **17.** 16 **18.** 9 **19.** 12 **20.** 0 **21.** 63 **22.** 35 **23.** 12 **24.** 42 **25.** 21 **26.** 24 **27.** 40 **28.** 32 **29.** 9 **30.** 45

Practice 8: **1.** 0 **2.** 63 **3.** 25 **4.** 18 **5.** 2 **6.** 24 **7.** 12 **8.** 0 **9.** 7 **10.** 6 **11.** 64 **12.** 45 **13.** 18 **14.** 27 **15.** 9 **16.** 6 **17.** 0 **18.** 4 **19.** 49 **20.** 20 **21.** 5 **22.** 21 **23.** 54 **24.** 0 **25.** 18 **26.** 3 **27.** 42 **28.** 72 **29.** 12 **30.** 36

Practice 9: **1.** 1 **2.** 56 **3.** 20 **4.** 18 **5.** 0 **6.** 8 **7.** 72 **8.** 8 **9.** 6 **10.** 10 **11.** 28 **12.** 0 **13.** 30 **14.** 21 **15.** 48 **16.** 12 **17.** 40 **18.** 32 **19.** 81 **20.** 0 **21.** 16 **22.** 0 **23.** 24 **24.** 12 **25.** 4 **26.** 15 **27.** 0 **28.** 27 **29.** 54 **30.** 36

Practice 10: **1.** 6 **2.** 4 **3.** 3 **4.** 9 **5.** 0 **6.** 6 **7.** 9 **8.** 5 **9.** 1 **10.** 7 **11.** 7 **12.** 2 **13.** 5 **14.** 8 **15.** 1 **16.** 9 **17.** 3 **18.** 3 **19.** 7 **20.** 3 **21.** 9 **22.** 2 **23.** 0 **24.** 6 **25.** 3 **26.** 6 **27.** 7 **28.** 4 **29.** 5 **30.** 9

Practice 11: **1.** 7 **2.** 8 **3.** 0 **4.** 2 **5.** 5 **6.** 8 **7.** 1 **8.** 3 **9.** 7 **10.** 2 **11.** 5 **12.** 5 **13.** 8 **14.** 6 **15.** 0 **16.** 4 **17.** 2 **18.** 3 **19.** 6 **20.** 1 **21.** 9 **22.** 8 **23.** 5 **24.** 2 **25.** 4 **26.** 0 **27.** 8 **28.** 7

29. 1 **30.** 5

Practice 12: **1.** 4 **2.** 6 **3.** 3 **4.** 1 **5.** 6 **6.** 4 **7.** 5 **8.** 2 **9.** 0 **10.** 8 **11.** 0 **12.** 8 **13.** 7 **14.** 9 **15.** 8 **16.** 1 **17.** 6 **18.** 3 **19.** 9 **20.** 0 **21.** 9 **22.** 1 **23.** 4 **24.** 0 **25.** 9 **26.** 4 **27.** 2 **28.** 4 **29.** 7 **30.** 1

Name _____

Achieving Facts Fluency Support Master 1

Ten-Frame

Name

Part-Part-Whole Mat

Name

Achieving Facts Fluency Support Master 3

Double Ten-Frames

Triangle Flash Cards

Achieving Facts Fluency Support Master 4

Name _____

Achieving Facts Fluency Support Master 5   **3-Section Spinner**

6-Section Spinner

Name _____

Achieving Facts Fluency Support Master 7   **Hundredths Square**

Name _____

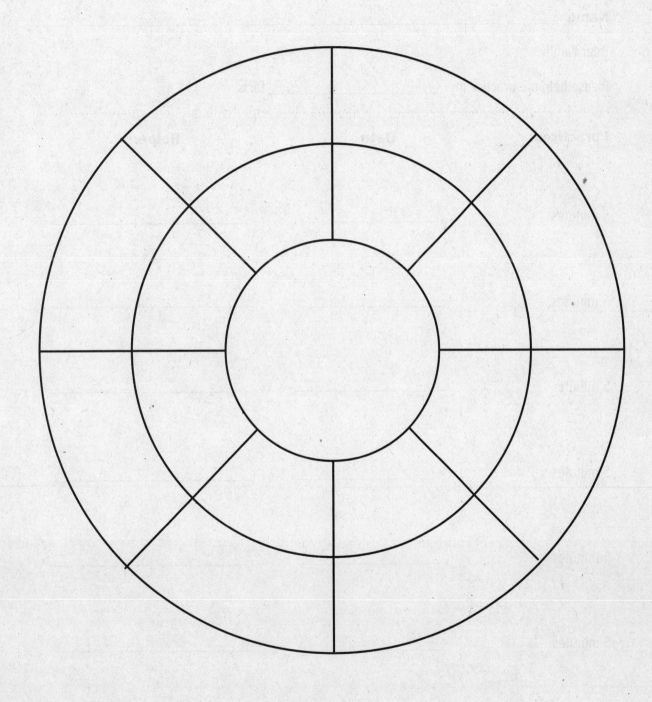

Practice Minutes Record

Name _____

Dear Family,

Please help me practice my _____ facts.

....

I practiced: **Date**   **Helper**

5 minutes   _____   _____

5 minutes   _____   _____

5 minutes   _____   _____

5 minutes   _____   _____

5 minutes   _____   _____

5 minutes   _____   _____

Return completed record to your teacher.

Practice Minutes Record

60 Minutes

Name _____

Dear Family,

Please help me practice my _____ • _____ facts.

....

New Facts

I practiced:	Date	Helper
5 minutes		
5 minutes		
5 minutes		
5 minutes		
5 minutes		
5 minutes		

Review Facts

I practiced:	Date	Helper
5 minutes		
5 minutes		
5 minutes		
5 minutes		
5 minutes		
5 minutes		

Return completed record to your teacher.

Practice Minutes Record

100 Minutes

Name _____

Dear Family,

Please help me practice my _____ facts.

....

New Facts

I practiced:	Date	Helper
10 minutes	_____	_____
10 minutes	_____	_____
10 minutes	_____	_____
10 minutes	_____	_____
10 minutes	_____	_____

Review Facts

I practiced:	Date	Helper
10 minutes	_____	_____
10 minutes	_____	_____
10 minutes	_____	_____
10 minutes	_____	_____
10 minutes	_____	_____

Return completed record to your teacher.

Achieving Facts Fluency Support Master 11   **Practice Minutes Record**

Practice Minutes Record

Name _____

Dear Family,

Please help me practice my _____ facts.

....

New Facts

I practiced:	Date	Helper
10 minutes	_____	_____
10 minutes	_____	_____
10 minutes	_____	_____
10 minutes	_____	_____
10 minutes	_____	_____
10 minutes	_____	_____

Review Facts

I practiced:	Date	Helper
10 minutes	_____	_____
10 minutes	_____	_____
10 minutes	_____	_____
10 minutes	_____	_____
10 minutes	_____	_____
10 minutes	_____	_____

Return completed record to your teacher.

Achieving Facts Fluency

30
Minutes

Practice Award

CONGRATULATIONS

Student's Name

on your hard work practicing your

_____ facts.

Teacher's Signature

Achieving Facts Fluency

60
Minutes

_____
Student's Name

CONGRATULATIONS

on your hard work practicing your _____ facts.

_____
Teacher's Signature

Practice Award

Achieving Facts Fluency

100 Minutes

CONGRATULATIONS

on your hard work practicing your

_____ facts.

_____
Student's Name

_____
Teacher's Signature

Achieving Facts Fluency

120 Minutes

_____
Student's Name

CONGRATULATIONS

on your hard work practicing your _____ facts.

_____
Teacher's Signature

Practice Award

Name _____

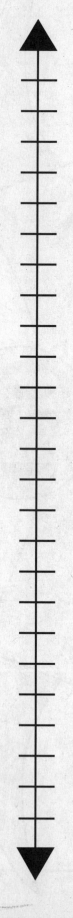

Achieving Facts Fluency Support Master 17

Number Lines

Name

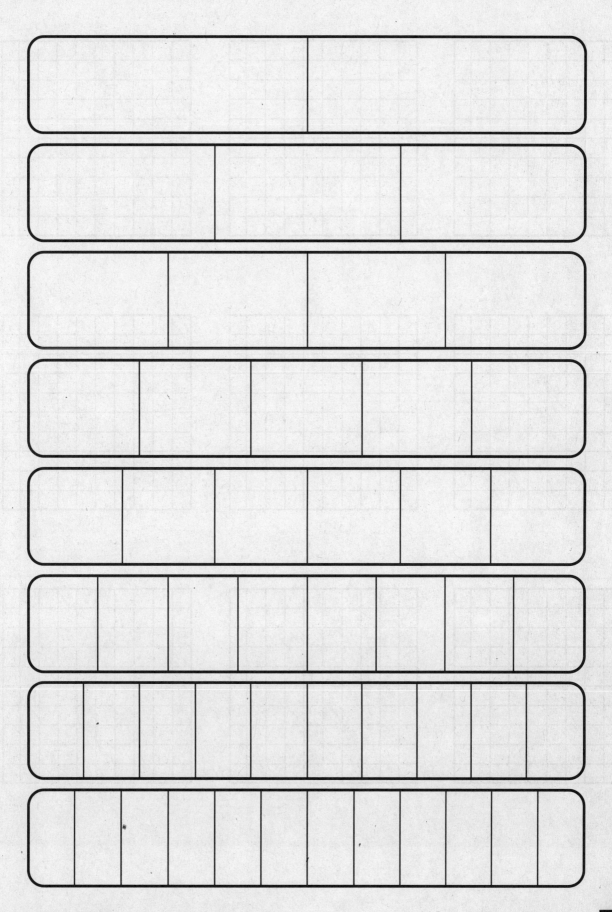

Name

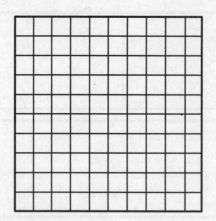 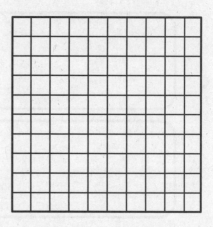

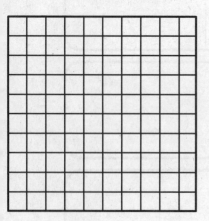 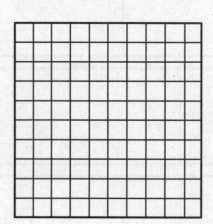 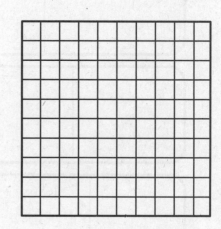

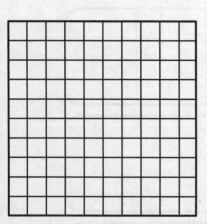 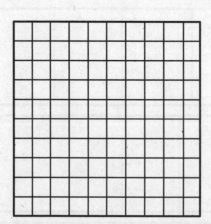 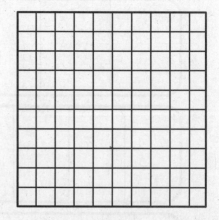

Achieving Facts Fluency Support Master 19   **Hundredths Squares**

My Math Handbook

Name _____ Date _____

This is what I learned today.

_____

_____

_____

_____

_____

_____

_____

Here's an example of what I learned.

Level _____ Workshop _____